Thetford Forest

Making a Landscape, 1922-1997

By Kate Skipper and Tom Williamson

ISBN 0-906219-45-0

Published by the Centre of East Anglian Studies,
University of East Anglia, Norwich NR4 7TJ

Designed and printed by Goodprint UK Limited 01842 761546

Acknowledgements

Many people have helped us with this book. We would like to thank colleagues and students at the Centre of East Anglian Studies, especially Janet Lister, Jill Ramsey, Susanna Wade Martins, Anthea Taigel, Chizuko Wesley, Mavis Wesley and Richard Wilson: and both employees, and former employees, of the Forestry Commission. Anna Chylac first encouraged our researches; Sandy Greig suggested that we turn them into a book, and provided much information about current forestry practices and policy. Thanks also to Mike Taylor, for information about modern harvesting. Figures 2 and 8 are reproduced courtesy of Derek Edwards, of Norfolk Landscape Archaeology: Figure 4 is reproduced courtesy of the Norfolk Record Office. Phillip Judge produced all of the diagrams, with his customary efficiency and good grace. Much of the information in this volume comes from `oral history' and we would like to thank the following for allowing themselves to be interviewed: Arthur Cadman, Graham Hobbs, Billy Steel, and Betty and Rex Witta. Thanks, in particular, to Alec Douet for conducting many of the interviews. Most of the photographs are from the Forestry Commission archives at Santon Downham. Figure 38 is by Phin Skipper.

Thetford Forest

Making a Landscape, 1922-1997

Contents

Chapter 1

Before the Forest

Chapter 1. Before the Forest

Introduction

Thetford Forest is one of East Anglia's most striking landscapes: covering more than 19,000 hectares, it is the largest area of pine woodland in lowland England. Here the visitor can find peace and solitude and can roam unhindered through what seems, in places, like a natural wilderness. Yet the forest is an entirely man-made landscape, and one of no great antiquity. Although it has incorporated and preserved relics of human activity going back thousands of years, the forest itself is a mere 75 years old: and this volume is written to celebrate its anniversary. We will try in the chapters that follow to explain how the forest came into existence and how it came to look the way it does. Landscape historians usually study the older features of the countryside - ancient woods and fields, the origins and development of villages and hamlets. But Thetford Forest, although entirely a child of the twentieth century, is no less worthy of our attention, not least because it is enjoyed by ever-increasing numbers of visitors. And as we shall see, although its history may be brief compared with most of England's many landscapes, it is nevertheless a complex, varied, and intriguing one, which encapsulates many features both of East Anglia's, and of Britain's, recent past.

As in all historical studies, in the pages that follow we make extensive use of documents, many of them preserved at the Forestry Commission's archives at Cambridge and Santon Downham. But in addition, the forest's relative modernity means that we have also been able to employ the technique of `oral history': that is, we have been able to talk to some of the people who worked in the forest in its earlier days, often thereby learning things which are absent from, or less clear in, the written sources.

The forest has a varied appearance. In some places, as in the area to the north or west of Thetford, the pines grow in almost continuous blocks for many hundreds of hectares. But elsewhere, as around Swaffham in the north or Harling to the east, the plantations are interspersed with open land - wide arable fields bounded by lines of twisted pines or flimsy hawthorn hedges, or pockets of heathland (Figure 1). But whether these surroundings impinge on the forest scene, or are invisible from it, some account of the history of this wider landscape, of the district known as *Breckland*, is essential before we can begin our main story.

The key to Breckland's history is its essentially marginal nature, born of its poor soils and harsh climate. The region comprises a low chalk plateau, rising to between 15 and 30 metres above sea level, which is cut by a number of prominent river valleys: those of the Thet, Little Ouse, Wissey, Nar, and Lark. It is bounded by the low Fenland to the west and by the higher claylands to the east. During the early Ice Ages the chalk was covered by chalky, stony deposits, left by an ice sheet coming from the north. During the harsh conditions of a subsequent glaciation (the Wolstonian) this material was first weathered, to produce a subsoil of gravel, chalk rubble, and sand; and then blanketed by deposits of wind-blown sand. In some places chalky deposits lie near to the surface, giving rise to alkaline, calcareous soils;

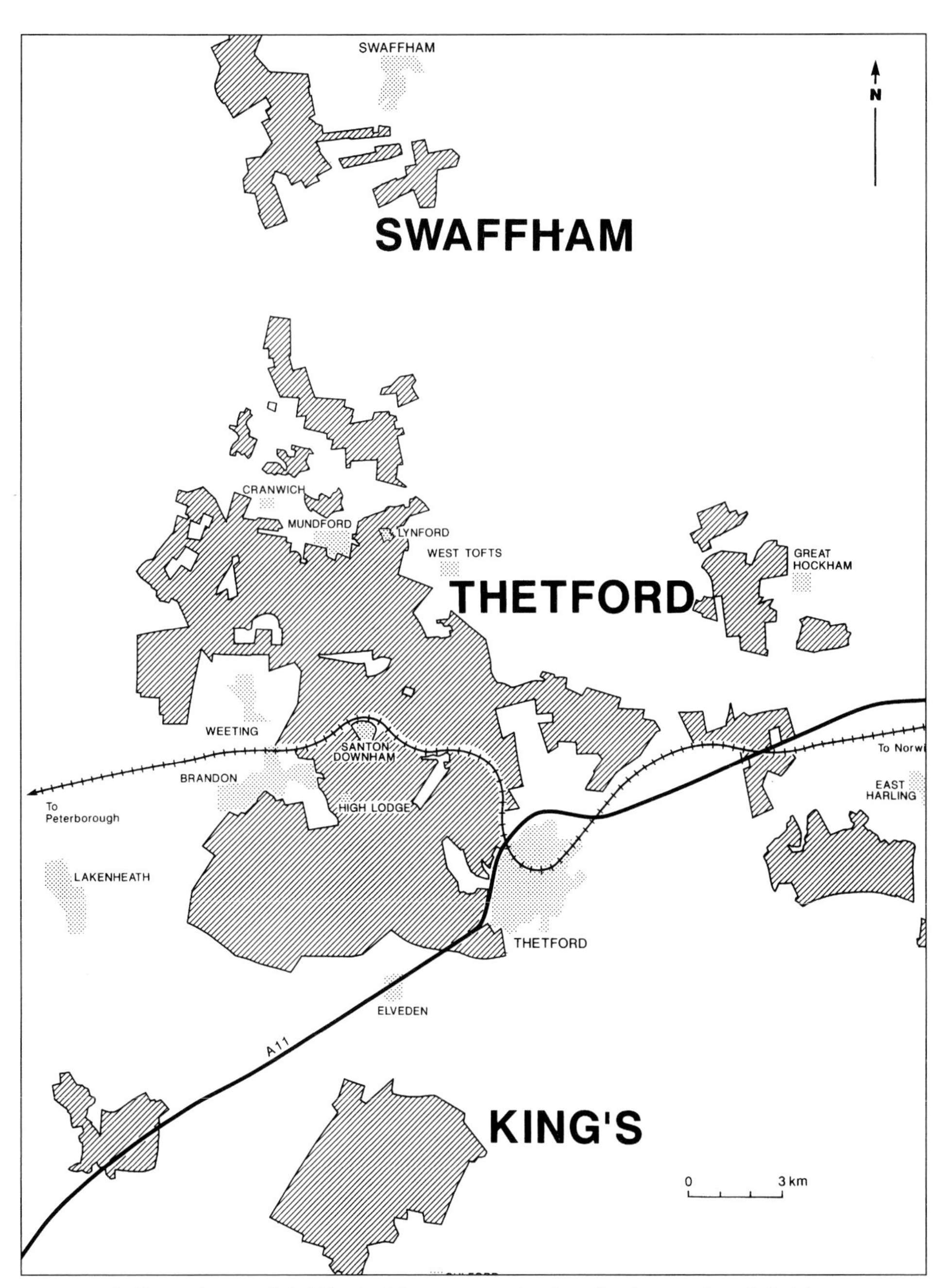

1. *General map of the Thetford Forest area, showing the three main subdivisions of the forest: Swaffham, Thetford and King's.*

but over much of the region the sand is two, three or more metres deep and the soils highly acidic. In either case, water is absorbed almost instantly after rain: not that the region receives much precipitation, being among the driest in all Britain. It is a harsh climate in other ways. It is, in particular, noted for its unseasonable frosts, which have been recorded in every month of the year.

The absorbent nature of the soil has ensured that in all periods people have chosen to live in the major valleys, beside the rivers which provide a reliable source of water. Here, too, the better, more calcareous soils are usually to be found. On the `uplands', in contrast, water is only available in a few places from the Breckland `meres' - strange pools fed from the chalk which fill and empty quite independently of the immediate pattern of rainfall.

Breckland's Early History

Breckland thus has a particularly harsh environment. It was, nevertheless, extensively colonised by woodland in the wake of the last Ice Age, which ended around fourteen thousand years ago, and by the time that Neolithic farmers settled here around 3,500 BC the area was occupied by a range of shrubs and trees, including oak, elm, hazel and lime. It used to be thought that this vegetation was rapidly cleared by these early farmers, but recent research suggests instead that the most extensive clearances were restricted to the major valleys. Here farmers made their settlements and laid out fields in which they cultivated emmer and barley. The higher ground continued to carry much tree cover although here too the land was gradually opened up, largely no doubt by the grazing of sheep, cattle and pigs, which prevented the regeneration of trees. The uplands were exploited in other ways. They were, in particular, mined for flints, most notably at Grimes Graves near Brandon. Several hectares of ground here are peppered with the remains of pits, dug

2. Aerial photograph of Grimes Graves, the Neolithic flint mines near Brandon (courtesy of Derek Edwards, Norfolk Landscape Archeology).

in places to a depth of 13 metres in order to reach the better-quality `floorstone' flint, which had networks of radiating tunnels fanning out from their base (Figure 2).

Although Breckland's soils are fairly infertile they are also easily cultivated: and as a result they were attractive to early settlers, who lacked a plough sophisticated enough to cultivate the more fertile, but much heavier, soils of the claylands to the east. During the later Neolithic period and in the Bronze Age clearance of the uplands proceeded apace, and the extent of exploitation and settlement are evident from the vast numbers of worked flints which can be picked up from the surface of the local fields. The most obvious trace left by these early farmers, however, are the numerous round barrows - burial mounds of early Bronze Age date - which still survive in many areas of unploughed heathland, and in places within the pine forest. Most are found on the dry uplands, probably because the dead were buried away from the main valley settlements, on the grazing grounds. Good examples can be seen on Brettenham Heath, or in the country park at Kilverstone.

During the Iron Age, Breckland continued to be fairly densely settled although by this time the heavier soils to the east were being opened up for cultivation. There was a major defended settlement at Thetford, its ramparts later incorporated into those of the medieval castle. There was also, by the end of the period, a large and enigmatic site on Gallows Hill, to the north of Thetford, comprising a number of concentric rectangular enclosures, filled in part with a dense pattern of upright posts: perhaps an artificial version of the kind of grove which, according to classical writers, Iron Age people used for meetings and worship. Certainly, by this time real woodland must have been in short supply in the region. The uplands had now been almost entirely cleared of trees, and farms and hamlets were widely scattered, although still largely restricted to the main valleys. In the Roman period, too, settlements were thick on the ground, with farms and villas densely clustered in the valleys, and with a number of substantial villages, at Icklingham, Hockwold and elsewhere.

Extensive early clearance of the woodland led to important changes in the character of Breckland's environment. We sometimes think of heaths as `natural' environments, but in Breckland as elsewhere they are essentially man-made. The region's soils, already poor and acidic, became steadily more so under the impact of human settlement. Clearance of woodland increased the impact of rainfall, encouraging the `leaching', or downward migration, of lime and other nutrients. Regular or periodic cultivation of the land hastened this process. A largely treeless landscape of heath and acid grassland gradually developed, separated by ribbons of arable land along the river valleys. The essential features of this landscape were to remain largely unchanged until the eighteenth and nineteenth centuries.

The Middle Ages

In the fifth and sixth centuries Breckland, like other areas of East Anglia, was settled by new peoples coming from north Germany and Scandinavia. The most important were the Angles, although other tribes were also represented - such as the Suebi, who

3. Thetford Warren Lodge, built in the late fifteenth century on the Prior of Thetford's warren to provide protection for the warrener and his stock of rabbits.

gave their name to Swaffham. The population of Britain was falling at this time, although the decline was much less severe in Breckland than in most other areas, for this was a time of technological regression, in which settlement seems to have retrenched once more onto the more easily cultivated soils. Indeed, to judge from the number and size of the cemeteries dating from this period - at Illington, Lackford and elsewhere - Breckland was relatively densely settled at this time. At West Stow the excavated and reconstructed Anglo-Saxon village provides a good impression of the kind of settlement occupied in this period. Here, on a low bluff above the river Lark, seven groups of buildings - each consisting of a substantial timber-built `hall' surrounded by a number of sunken-floored buildings - were occupied by farmers who grew wheat, barley and peas and kept sheep, cattle, pigs and goats.

Yet as the centuries passed, as population recovered and cultivation expanded once more on heavier and more fertile land, Breckland became an increasingly marginal area. Domesday Book shows it as the most sparsely-occupied area in eastern England. The `hundreds' - the administrative subdivisions of the Anglo-Saxon shires - are larger here than elsewhere in East Anglia, testifying to the relative poverty, and low population density, of the region. But it was nevertheless carefully farmed, and by the thirteenth century had developed an economy which made the most of what natural advantages it possessed. Well-connected by river transport to important distant markets, Breckland became a major centre for barley production. As in earlier periods the main areas of arable land were in the principal valleys, close to the villages which, for the most part, comprised rather sprawling clusters of farms and cottages. Most of the ploughland lay in open fields, that is, the holdings of each farmer did not lie in compact hedged fields but were instead splintered in a myriad of unhedged strips, intermixed with those of his neighbours.

In addition to the permanent arable in the open fields Breckland villages usually had areas of `breaks', that is, portions of poorer land which were brought into cultivation on a regular but sporadic basis, cultivated for a few years, and then allowed to tumble back to heathland once more. As in earlier periods, however, the uplands were largely occupied by areas of open heath where sheep were grazed by day. By night they were folded on the arable fields, after these had been harvested or when they lay fallow: here they dropped dung and compacted the soil with their feet. This process of `tathing' ensured a constant flow of nutrients from the heaths to the ploughland, and thus allowed the farmers to keep the thin soils in cultivation.

Other, more specialised uses of the heaths were developing by this time: some were used as rabbit warrens by manorial lords. Rabbits, introduced into England soon after the Norman Conquest, were greatly valued for their fur and meat, and rabbit farms made good use of this rather marginal land, the rabbits burrowing freely in the loose dry soil. A lease for Brandon Warren, dating from 1563, described how it was `very Wyde and Large but of very Baren Soyle and nevertheless very good for brede of Conyes'. The rabbits were carefully managed, fed over the winter, systematically culled and protected from predators.

In late medieval times, following the Black Death and associated disasters of the mid fourteenth century, the population declined. With less demand for cereal crops, the area of arable land contracted and that of heaths and, in particular, warrens expanded. Oxwickfield, one of the outfield `breaks' of Brandon, thus became a permanent warren. Indeed, although farming was in a state of recession in the region in the fifteenth century the warrens boomed. Landlords invested substantial sums in these enterprises. They built lodges to house the warrener and his equipment, often substantial structures to provide protection against attack by poachers, like the one which still survives (although in a ruinous condition) near Thetford (Figure 3). The warrens were bounded by substantial banks or sometimes by a series of banks, to prevent the rabbits escaping or making raids on the crops of neighbouring farmers. Good examples can be seen in a number of places within the forest. Those near the Forest Centre at High Lodge, the triple banks marking the boundary of Downham High Lodge Warren, are particularly impressive.

As the population fell many of the villages located on the poorer soils in Breckland declined in size, as farmers drifted off to seek holdings in more attractive locations. The process was a slow one, which continued into the sixteenth and seventeenth centuries and in many cases led to the complete disappearance of the villages, leaving only a ruined church, the manor house, and a cottage or two to mark where a community had once existed. The central core of Breckland is peppered with such places: West Tofts, Buckenham Tofts and Lynford are now names on the map, rather than villages.

The Phase of `Improvement'

The population decline of the late medieval and early post-medieval periods paved the way for the next phase of Breckland's history. From the mid seventeenth to the late nineteenth century, Breckland was dominated, as almost no other region in East Anglia, by large landed estates. They flourished here because land was cheap: the

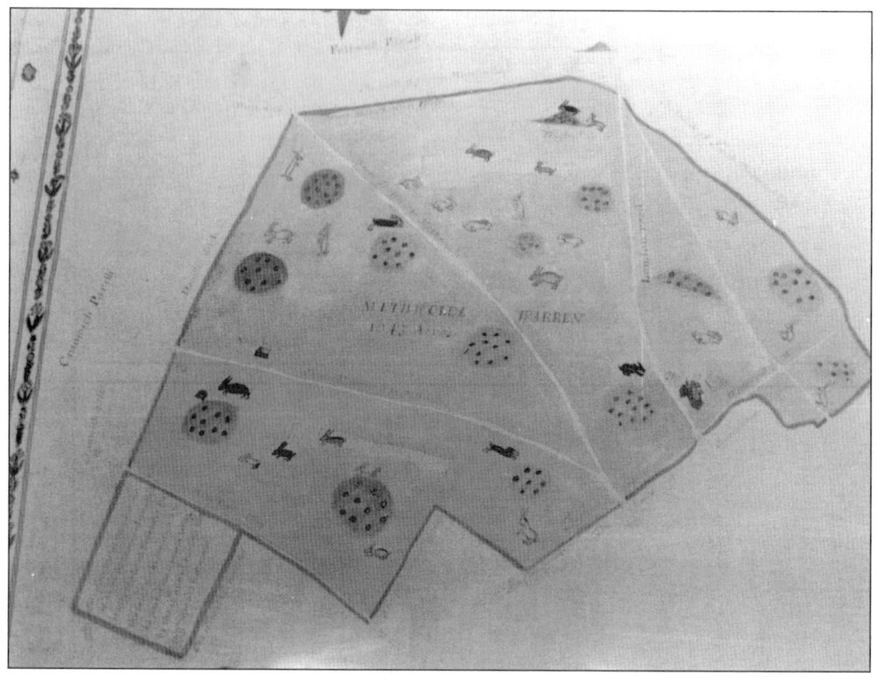

4. Methwold Warren, as depicted on a map of 1699

gentry systematically bought up the holdings of smaller landowners, accelerating the process of village depopulation. The relative cheapness of land often attracted landowners of a particular kind. Although some families remained here for several generations, many estates were purchased by individuals who had made their fortunes outside East Anglia, in trade or industry. Men like `Mr Vincent', an officer in the excise who erected a magnificent house and elaborate gardens at Buckenham Tofts in the late seventeenth century: or Mr Lyne Stephens, `the richest commoner in England', who settled at Lynford with his wife - a French Catholic ballet dancer - in the 1850s.

The impact of the large estates on the Breckland landscape was profound. Their owners built and rebuilt great mansions on an often lavish scale: they laid out fine gardens and extensive parks. Some of these places have now entirely disappeared, their mansions demolished and their grounds buried under the Forestry Commission plantations: like Santon Downham Hall, which stood near the main Forestry Commission offices at Downham. Others survive only in relict form, like Buckenham Tofts, where the hall was demolished in 1946 but the great park - one of the finest in Norfolk - still survives, and is indeed well-maintained by the army, in whose training ground it now lies. Many, however, still exist, such as Euston, with its grounds landscaped by both William Kent and Capability Brown; or Lynford, rebuilt in the 1850s to a design by William Burn, and with magnificent terraced gardens by William Andrews Nesfield. Such was the scale of building and landscaping in this period that it is probably no exaggeration to say that the history of English country house architecture, and of landscape design, could be written solely on the basis of Breckland examples.

Eighteenth- and nineteenth-century landowners had a wider impact on the landscape, however. From the early years of the eighteenth century they were increasingly involved in the `improvement' of their estates, investing substantial sums of money in the enclosure of open fields and heaths and in large-scale schemes of land reclamation. At the start of the eighteenth century the majority of Breckland was still unenclosed - an open, largely hedgeless landscape of arable fields and heaths. Over the following century-and-a-half much of this was to change. In some places, large landowners indulged in a veritable spending spree of property acquisition, systematically buying out their smaller neighbours so that they could pursue schemes of enclosure and improvement unhampered by opposition or dissent. Such `engrossment' seems to have continued in many parts of Breckland throughout the late seventeenth and eighteenth centuries. Thus a series of maps for Sapiston in Suffolk shows the gradual purchase and exchange of freehold strips and glebe land by the Dukes of Grafton from 1667 to 1789. The parish was completely enclosed without a Parliamentary act, and the map accompanying the act for the neighbouring parish of Honington (1801) refers to Sapiston as `recently enclosed'. Between 1760 and 1798 Lord Cornwallis similarly set out to buy the parishes of Culford, Ingham, Timworth, and West Stow: by 1800 the estate controlled the entire area of all five parishes: they were surveyed, and then divided into large new farms, mostly covering more than 1,000 acres (c.400 hectares) each.

Although enclosure continued in this piecemeal way throughout the seventeenth and eighteenth centuries Breckland was nevertheless effected more than any other region in East Anglia by Parliamentary enclosure: that is, by enclosure brought about by passing an act in Parliament empowering commissioners to survey and reallot property in a parish, completely extinguishing all common rights and removing all commons. Of the 126 parishes in the region, 66 had Parliamentary enclosure acts. In most cases well over half of the area of the parish was enclosed: and the great majority of acts dealt with open fields as well as with commons. In all, around 60% of the total land area of the region was enclosed by Parliamentary act, mostly in the two decades either side of 1800 when - due to rising population and the Napoleonic War blockade - agricultural prices were particularly high, and farmers and landowners in an optimistic mood.

Enclosure was one aspect of the process historians call the `agricultural revolution'. This also featured the adoption of new forms of husbandry, involving regular rotations of turnips, cereals and clover. Clover fixed Nitrogen - essential for crop growth - directly in the soil from the atmosphere. It also provided summer grazing and - together with the turnips - fodder for winter feed. No longer were fields left fallow (uncultivated) every third or fourth year, to be grazed and `tathed' by the great Breckland flocks. Instead, new, more docile breeds of sheep, less adapted to life on the open heath and the long nightly trek to the fold, were grazed on grass or clover `leys', and on turnips, in the arable fields. Cattle were also now kept in larger numbers, fed over winter on turnips in yards where their manure steadily accumulated. These new crops and new forms of livestock management supplied the nutrients necessary for arable farming. The vast areas of heathland grazing were no longer necessary to sustain husbandry, and their reclamation began in earnest. Marl (or `clay' as it was locally known) - the underlying deposits of chalk and chalk rubble - was excavated from deep pits and systematically applied to the reclaimed land, in order to neutralise soil acidity. The maps drawn up to accompany the improvements planned by the Walsingham estate in Stanford and Sturston in the 1770s noted possible sites for digging clay and marl, indicated by such captions as `chalk at 6 foot' and `good clay at 4 foot'. Marl was also applied to existing arable land: this was an old practice but was now adopted on a much larger scale than ever before. In 1786 the Duke of Grafton described how `The more valuable and fruitful parts' of his Euston farm had `been made so at the expense of a thorough coat of clay found in many places upon it'. This was large-scale manipulation of the natural soil environment, and some of the side effects were unexpected, and far from beneficial, as the agricultural writer Hugh Raynbird described in 1849.

Although marl has been found ... most excellent for wheat, yet a sad mortality in the sheep has been observed whilst feeding on land that has recently been marled.

Estate records from the early nineteenth century make a number of references to the problem. Thus Mr Fox of Tottington - a tenant of the Walsingham estate - sustained great losses `by sheep warping [aborting] their lambs last year'. Mr Lincoln, a neighbouring tenant, claimed in 1836 that he had lost 200 lambs `being warped in consequence of claying land'.

In innumerable ways, eighteenth- and nineteenth-century landowners threw themselves wholeheartedly into the business of reclamation and improvement. New roads were laid out, farm buildings were rebuilt on a grand scale, and the new fields surrounded with trim hawthorn hedges or - in the nineteenth century - by hedges of Scots pine, locally known as `Deal Rows'. Most of these have now grown up to form the lines of romantic, twisted, gnarled trees which are so characteristic a feature of the Breckland scene (only a tiny proportion, including the fine example beside the A11 near Elveden, are still managed as hedges).

Landowners were eager to experiment with a range of new techniques. Some adopted the practice of irrigating or `floating' water meadows, a method which had up to this time been largely restricted to the west of England. By dressing meadows with a continuous film of moving water in the winter months, grass growth was accelerated and livestock were provided with an `early bite' in March. In May the animals were removed, irrigation recommenced, and a greatly enhanced hay crop was taken in June. The characteristic earthworks associated with this practice - parallel ridges running across low-lying grass fields - can still be seen in a number of places in Breckland. Most attempts at `floating' appear to have been short-lived, however: in spite of aristocratic enthusiasm, the technique is poorly adapted to East Anglia, with its sharp late frosts. Indeed, in other ways it is apparent that not all forms of `improvement' carried out in this period made practical, economic sense. Not all landowners were motivated by rational economic considerations, but rather by a boundless optimism, and by an earnest desire to `make the desert bloom'. `Improvement' was often seen as an end in itself, a duty, a mission. When in 1774 Thomas de Grey bemoaned the costs of enclosing the heaths at Tottington he observed candidly that the `great expense ... would but ill answer, unless there was a real satisfaction in employing the labourers and bringing forth a ragged dirty parish to a neatness of cultivation'.

Improvement and reclamation could be a risky business in this difficult landscape: the extreme marginality of the soils was exacerbated by the climatic extremes which characterised the region. In 1786 de Grey remarked 'Our farms in the open country have suffered much by two dry summers and a winter unusually severe. I will venture to assert they are worth less by 20% than three years ago'.

In 1828 John Worledge of Ingham described the farms in his area to a House of Lords Committee as `principally of poor sandy soil and gravelly land, the produce of which in corn is very precarious, amounting in dry seasons to little or nothing'. Not

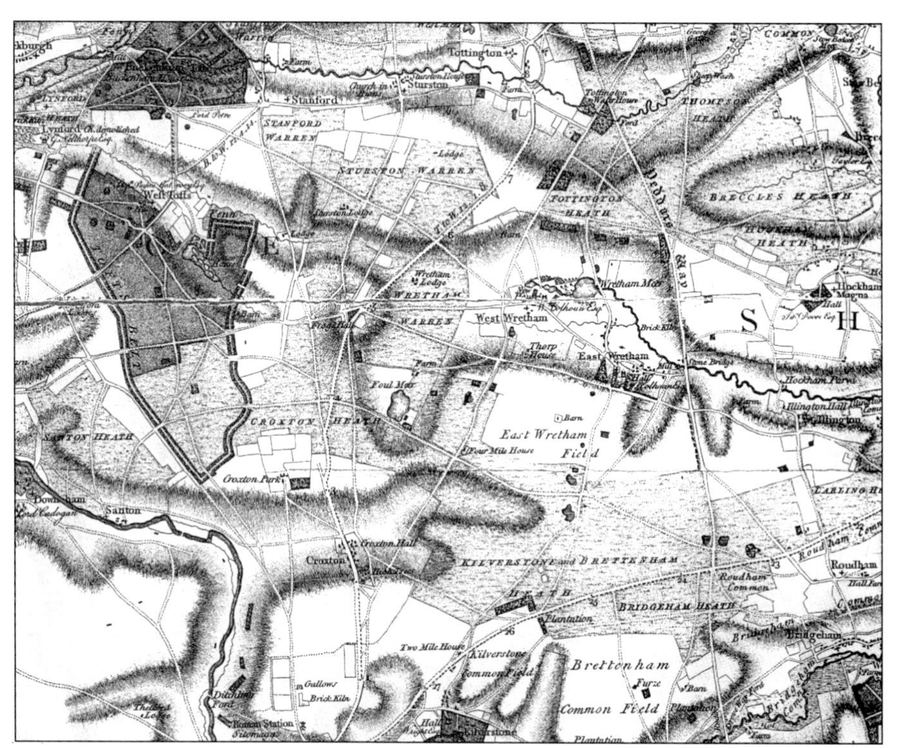

5. The area to the north of Thetford, as shown on Faden's map of Norfolk, 1797. Note the large parks (dark shading), surviving areas of 'common field', and extensive tracts of heath and warren.

surprising, then, that large areas of heathland continued to survive; nor that much of the new arable land reverted to grass (albeit improved grass) when prices declined from their dizzy peak in the immediate aftermath of the Napoleonic Wars.

Nor did all aspects of the old economy of Breckland disappear. Much arable land continued to be farmed as arable 'breaks', even after closure. Many rabbit warrens continued to function, because on the poorer soils they continued to make good economic sense. Even in the 1780s some warrens were expanding at the expense of arable land. Thus in March 1784 William Smith, a tenant of the Walsingham estate, was given permission to `add to his present warren in Sturston 48 acres [c.20 hectares] of the arable lands belonging to the farm of the said Wm Smith adjoining to the north side of his warren bank and use the land as a warren during the continuation of his lease'. Many warrens continued to be massive concerns: that at Stanford covered more than 537 acres (217 hectares) in 1820 and was stocked with 7,200 rabbits. Including the rabbits taken from the adjoining arable and sheepwalk the numbers were even greater: nearly fifteen thousand were taken between 17 August 1824 and 1 Marsh 1825, a yield which was considered about average. The existence of such feral populations might in turn discourage the expansion of arable farming. Tenants of land adjacent to warrens were for ever bemoaning the depredations of rabbits. When the future of the Walsingham's Stanford farm was being debated in 1782 it was specifically stated that, because it was bordered by the warrens of Wretham and Sturston, it was likely that `the greater part of it will be made a rabbit farm'.

Of course, eighteenth- and nineteenth-century landowners were not solely interested in agriculture. They were also obsessed with shooting, and this addiction also encouraged the retention of heathland. Abel Smith, a troublesome tenant of the Merton estate in the early nineteenth century, was accused of having

Cleared all the furze off Wether heath, which leaves it as naked as Lincoln Inn Square for the protection of game, and threatens to plough up the whole heath unless he is given permission to plough 30 acres.

One of the complaints made in 1817 about Mr Sewell, a difficult tenant of the Walsingham estate, was that he had ploughed up areas of heath land without permission, and had thus damaged the game cover.

It was partly to provide cover for game (particularly for pheasants) that many areas of woodland came to be planted in Breckland in the course of the eighteenth and nineteenth centuries. Woods and plantations extended out from the parks and gardens of the gentry on to the barren open heaths. Although the extent of afforestation was relatively minor compared with what was to be achieved by the Forestry Commission in the twentieth century, the region seems to have witnessed more tree-planting than almost any other part of East Anglia. Notable examples include the great belt of trees established in the 1770s at West Tofts, which embraced not only the park but also the home farm and a portion of heathland. It consisted of a variety of trees, although principally conifers, and covered an area of around 100 hectares. Arthur Young reported in 1804 how Sylvanus Bevan, a noted agricultural improver, had planted no less than 966,000 trees on his estate at Riddlesworth.

As well as supplying cover for game, plantations had an important aesthetic role: and it is noteworthy that the most extensive plantations were associated with parks and pleasure grounds in the immediate vicinity of gentlemen's residences. But contemporaries were also well aware of the practical and economic benefits of tree-planting. Plantations provided shelter for crops and livestock in this bare and open landscape: more importantly, the wood and timber were a good long-term investment. The West Tofts belt was up for sale with the rest of the estate in 1780, and the Sale Particulars - having described the beauty of the trees in glowing terms - went on to assert that:

The number of trees that will remain in the Plantations, after they are thinned so as to leave them at a proper distance, to facilitate their Growth, will be about Six Hundred Thousand: which in the Course of a few years, will at least be worth a shilling a Tree, and consequently amount to Thirty Thousand Pounds'.

Even allowing for the customary exaggerations of sale catalogues, there can be no doubt that on marginal land like this large-scale tree-planting offered a better return in the medium term than agricultural rents. The `shilling a tree' quoted in 1780 refers to semi-mature specimens - the belt had only been planted a few years before. When mature they could be expected to fetch more than five times this amount. Nevertheless, the extent of afforestation in this period was limited, largely because of the risks involved on these light, acid, sandy soils. Trees failed not only because of drought and unseasonable frosts, but also because of the attacks of rabbits. Letters relating to the Buckenham Tofts and West Tofts estates in the 1780s describe in some detail the attempts made to keep rabbit numbers down prior to planting: they remained `beyond belief', considering that the owner, Payne Galway, had a warrener employed full time on the problem with `ferrets and near a hundred traps'.

The Breckland landscape as we see it today, outside the bounds of Thetford Forest itself, is largely a product of this phase of eighteenth and nineteenth-century improvement. The pattern of neat rectangular fields, the numerous marl pits, the substantial farms, farmyards, and workers cottages of brick and flint - are all, to a large extent, the result of the fashionable aristocratic enthusiasm for agriculture, the optimism and wealth of farmers - and the hard work of labourers. It is particularly important to emphasise the extent of reclamation in this period, in all parts of Breckland, because it is still often suggested, or implied, that prior to the activities of the Forestry Commission in the 1920s the region was a wilderness of open heathland, scarcely touched by the hand of man since prehistoric times. The sentiments expressed by H.J. Massingham in the 1920s are typical:

With the exception of Breckland, an area of 400 square miles, all, or nearly all, our wildernesses are pools, not lakes or inland seas of apartness. I once went for a walk on the Brecks with [W.G.] Clarke ... the Brecks that day gave me an inkling of what it meant to wander forty years in the Desert...

In reality, much of this wildness was the consequence of quite recent changes: for the landscape of improvement was fragile and precarious, sustained by economic circumstances which changed rapidly, and radically, from the late 1870s.

The Landscape of Agricultural Depression

As long as agriculture remained buoyant the great estates, with their mansions and parks, their farms and fields, could flourish in this hostile land. But from the late 1870s agricultural prices fell, as the home market was flooded with imports of grain (and later, refrigerated meat) from America and elsewhere. As agricultural profits plummeted so too did farm rents, and substantial areas of the poorer land begin to go out of cultivation. The extent of the change is clear on the Second Edition OS 6" maps surveyed in the first decades of the twentieth century. Many show extensive areas of heathland divided by field boundaries, and liberally scattered with marl pits: areas which had clearly been arable land until the depression, a fact which can generally be confirmed by examining earlier maps. Of course, not all the heathland in Breckland developed in this way: vast acreages, as already noted, had escaped reclamation and improvement in the eighteenth and nineteenth centuries. Nor was the increase in the area of heath in the late nineteenth centuries simply a case of agricultural retrenchment. In some ways it is best considered as a form of diversification, with estates placing more emphasis on shooting, and on the leasing of shooting rights, and less on arable agriculture. As Lord Walsingham observed to Rider Haggard, the owners of Breckland estates were able to `muddle along' on the proceeds from their sporting amenities, for `the majority of owners in that district would receive no advantage from their land if not for its suitability for the purpose of game rearing'. Partridges and pheasants were not now the only, or even the main, quarry. The numbers of wild rabbits had now increased to such an extent (aided by the success of gamekeepers in controlling their main predators) that they could be shot for sport on a large scale. Many Breckland estates were let on a regular basis during the shooting season. Land prices in the area were to some extent sustained by the popularity of shooting as a pastime among the rich, for it made the region a desirable place in which to live for all or part of the year. The Elveden Hall estate was purchased by Maharajah Duleep Singh in 1863 and under him the annual `bag' reached 9,400 partridges, 9,600 pheasants, 3,000 hares - and no less than 75,000 rabbits. In 1894 the estate was bought by Lord Iveagh and by the end of the century farming had become a minor activity. Half the land on the estate was given over to wild rabbit warrens.

Rabbit-farming and game-shooting might, to an improving agriculturalist, appear to be archaic or wasteful uses of land, but in this hostile environment they represented fairly rational forms of land use and could bring real financial rewards. In 1877, at the start of the agricultural depression, the income from game and rabbit-farming combined contributed no less than £1774.16.6 to the income of the Merton estate. The proportion of estate income from these sources rose steadily in subsequent years. As farming declined in importance in Breckland, rabbit numbers steadily increased - they were actively encouraged on most estates - and increasingly it was wild rabbits, rather than rabbits kept in warrens, which supplied the local firms of furriers, the most important of which was Lingwoods, with their highly automated factory at Brandon.

Diversification into rabbits and game was not the only way in which Breckland landowners attempted to weather the depression. The more enterprising farmers tried cultivating asparagus, blackcurrants and other market garden crops suited to this light soil. But such enterprises were precarious before the advent of large-scale field irrigation, and in an atmosphere of continuing gloom, arable progressively tumbled down to grass, heath, and wildness.

Chapter 2

Acquiring the Forest

Chapter 2. Acquiring the Forest

The Birth of the Commission

By the end of the First World War the economic position of large landed estates in England generally was very poor. Low agricultural prices, and therefore low rents, combined with social and political changes, meant that possession of an extensive landed estate was now often more of a liability than an asset. The problems of large landowners were particularly acute in areas of poor soil like Breckland: after a brief revival of agricultural fortunes during the First World War, slump returned with a vengeance. Farms were left untenanted, land became derelict. It was into these landscapes that a new force was introduced in the early 1920s: the Forestry Commission.

In 1916 the Prime Minister, H.H. Asquith, appointed the Forestry Sub-Committee of the Ministry of Reconstruction:

> *To consider and report upon the best means of conserving and developing the woodland and forestry resources of the United Kingdom, having regard to the experience gained during the War*

- when curtailment of timber imports had forcibly drawn attention to the limited extent, and poor condition, of the nation's woods and plantations. The committee, chaired by F.D. Acland, reported that the shortage of home-grown timber was indeed acute, with woodland accounting for less than 5% of the nation's land area; that this had important economic and strategic implications; that large areas of Britain were under-utilised; and that their afforestation would help sustain rural populations. The committee proposed that, over the following eighty years, no less than 1,770,000 acres (c.72,000 hectares) of land should be planted with trees. One and a half million acres of this should be by direct state purchase and planting, the rest through private enterprise, or by joint public/private schemes. The committee further recommended that a budget of £3,418,000 should be set aside for these purposes over the following decade. These recommendations were accepted by the Cabinet, and in 1918 an Interim Forestry Authority was appointed. The Forestry Bill was introduced in parliament in July 1919 and the Act received Royal Assent on 19 August. This authorised the appointment of eight Forestry Commissioners, charged with the duty of promoting all aspects of forestry in Britain. They were, among other things, empowered to acquire property; and to lease or sell any part of such land which, once acquired, was unsuitable for afforestation. Nearly three and half million pounds was to be paid into the Forestry Fund in the first decade of the Commission's existence.

This grand plan did not, however, proceed smoothly. On 6 December 1919 the Treasury gave general approval for the Commission to acquire land for afforestation at a rent which did not exceed 6s per acre per annum, or at a price not exceeding £6 per acre freehold. Some 50,000 acres (c.20,000 hectares) were acquired before the deepening post-War recession caused a rapid change in policy. The

Commission was allowed to purchase a further 55,000 acres in areas which had been hit particularly badly by mass unemployment, but even this was stopped in March 1921 and later that year the Commission's general authority to purchase land was rescinded altogether. The Geddes Committee, appointed to find where cuts in state expenditure could best be carried out, recommended that the whole policy adopted in 1919 should be scrapped. But the threat was fought off and in 25 July 1922, in an improving financial climate, the Treasury agreed to cancel the suspension of general authority although it nevertheless advised, in September, that the maximum purchase price for land should not exceed £3 per acre, and that no more than 3s per acre annum should be expended on leased land. This instruction was yet again changed in November 1922, with the upper limits now set at £4 per acre for freehold land, 3s 6d per annum for leased - although annual purchases were not to exceed 20,000 acres (c.8,100 hectares). The vacillations in government policy which were to dog the Commission's activities (in the Breckland, and more generally) throughout its history were thus evident from the very beginning.

Buying Breckland

Nevertheless, in a more stable financial climate the work of the Forestry Commission began in earnest and its attention soon turned to the increasingly derelict landscape of the East Anglian Breckland (Figure 6). In 1922 the first purchases were made here, beginning with a small area near Swaffham and, soon afterwards, 3,149 acres (1,275 hectares) of the Elveden estate. The 4,944 acre Downham Hall estate was bought from the National Provincial Building Society in 1923, and this was followed by the purchase of Lynford (6,208 acres, c.2,500 hectares) and part of Beechamwell (822 acres, c.330 hectares) in 1924. In March 1924, 1,570 acres (635 hectares) of the abortive Ministry of Agriculture demonstration farm at Methwold was transferred to the Commission: £45,360 had been spent on this enterprise before the Ministry concluded, as Nathaniel Kent had done over a century before, that the land was fit for little other than rabbits. The Commission continued to buy land at a steady rate

6. Bridgham Heath, looking north from the A11. Note in the distance the line of Scots pines, an outgrown former hedge

over the following three years. In 1925 the Cockley Cley estate, and parts of the Croxton and Didlington estates, were purchased; in 1926 it acquired the Weeting estate; and in 1927 further portions of the Didlington and Croxton estates were bought. By this time the Thetford Forest was the largest and fastest-expanding property in the Commission's domain.

But once again, changes in government policy led to a halt in further expansion. In 1928 10,396 acres (4,200 hextares) of the Croxton Hall estate, much of which had been leased for several years by the Commission, was offered for sale for as little as £3 per acre, including 85 houses and cottages and a respectable amount of standing timber. But the Commission's Divisional Officer reported that 'On account of financial stringency it was made apparent ... that the necessary money could not at present be found by the Forestry Commission'.

Various complex schemes were thought up to facilitate the purchase. It was proposed that the land should be bought in conjunction with the Ministry of Labour; or that it should be taken over by the Inland Revenue in lieu of the Estate Duties owed by the owner, Colonel MacKenzie. Finally, the Commissioners of Crown Land agreed to purchase the estate and lease it back to the Commission. The price eventually agreed with MacKenzie's trustees, after an independent valuation, was a snip at £33,000. In 1930 Sir Guy Nugent's West Harling estate (3,077 acres, 1,245 hectares) and a further portion of Lynford were purchased, together with 2,025 acres (820 hectares) of the Hockham Hall estate. After this, however, there was a lull in acquisitions. In 1931, the Commission's national budget was again reduced, land purchases were concentrated elsewhere in the country, and only small quantities of land (like the property of 176 acres at Feltwell, acquired in 1933) were bought during the early 1930s in the Thetford area.

It will be clear from this brief description that most of the land acquired by the Forestry Commission in Breckland in the 1920s and 30s came in large blocks. Indeed, more than 80% of the land in Thetford Forest was acquired from large landed estates: principally those of Beechamwell, Cockley Cley, Feltwell, Weeting, Didlington, West Harling, Downham, Croxton, Elveden, and Lynford. Given the prominence of large estates in the region in the early twentieth century, this is perhaps unsurprising. But it was rare for the Commission to approach landowners with purchase in mind. Usually it was the other way round. Estate owners were eager to sell, given the poor nature of the land and the impoverished state of their finances. And the sums paid for the land were, by modern standards, very low. The surviving documents show that the Commission were intent on driving a hard bargain and usually succeeded. Property on the Feltwell estate was thus valued at £405 by the Commission's surveyors but was actually purchased for £330. Prices were almost invariably below even the £4 per acre stipulated in 1922, with £2 4s 8d per acre being paid for the Downham Hall estate (excluding the money spent on the estate buildings); £3 10s for Weeting in 1926; and just over £3 per acre for Croxton in 1929. These low prices have become legendary in the Breckland area and although there is no truth in the oft-repeated myth that the Commission bought much of the land here for as little as 2s 6d per acre they certainly obtained it cheaply, and realised as much at the time. Billy Steel, who worked in the forests and nurseries in the 1920s, recalled the time when he met Sir William Taylor, the Chairman of the Commission, up from London on a tour of the West Harling estate.

> *`Do you know, Steel', he said, `the timber that came off Fifty Acre Plantation bought the whole estate' ... And he laughed and said: `Whoever was agent for the Nugent estate really fell down there'.*

Buying land might nevertheless involve long and complex negotiations, and estates were sometimes acquired in several stages. The purchase of the Lynford Hall estate is a good example. This property, which extended over 7,718 acres (3123 hectares), was advertised for sale in the Times in 1924 and described in predictably glowing terms. `As a shooting estate Lynford Hall ranks with the best still entire in East Anglia': as many as 27,000 rabbits had been killed there during the previous season. The original intention was to sell the whole estate at auction but shortly before this was to have taken place one Walter Abel Towler, a Cambridgeshire farmer and land speculator, bought the entire property by private treaty from the owner, J.O. Montague. It is possible that Towler always intended to re-sell the estate to the Commission. He certainly approached them soon after the purchase and - following what had become standard procedure - a representative of the Commission's Divisional Office went down to investigate, and drew up a report. He described how the hall had been occupied by the War Office during the war but had nevertheless been restored to good order. There were around 1,345 acres (544 hectares) of mixed plantations of various ages on the estate, including around 200 acres (80 hectares) of young woodland. Although these had not been properly maintained in recent years they were still, he estimated, worth between £40 and £45 per acre. The report paid careful attention to the area's soil and climatic conditions, and concluded that the whole estate could either be planted successfully or resold at a profit. It recommended that the property should be worked as one forest estate, in one or two units or `beats', but would ultimately form part of a larger unit. Any cottages and premises not required for employees (there were around 100 dwellings on the estate) were to be sold off immediately at an estimated price of around £14,000. The shooting rights were worth £1,000 per annum although it was estimated that this total would fall by between a quarter and a third if the existing plantations were felled. The plan at this stage was to sell the tenanted farms - which occupied an area of only 2,000 acres (800 hectares) - and to retain the rest: that is, the park, pleasure grounds, plantations, home farm, heaths and rough ground. Five thousand acres (c.2,000 hectares) of this area were to be planted with trees and the remaining portion divided up to form smallholdings for forest workers. In the event, however, the Commission was only able to purchase a part (although the greater part) of the estate - 6,208 acres of the original 7,718 on offer. Towler sold the remaining 1,510 acres to the Country Breeding Estates Co. Ltd. The profit made by Towler in these transactions is unknown but even in these unpropitious times speculating in large landed properties could prove very lucrative. A few years before, in 1917, Towler had bought the Bylaugh estate in mid-Norfolk and sold it on, within a few weeks, at a profit of £7,000!

In 1929, five years after they had purchased their portion of the estate from Towler, the Country Breeding Estates Company sold the bulk of it (935 acres) to the Commission. This included Lynford hall itself, a substantial `Jacobethan' mansion designed by the architect William Burn (and with gardens by W.A. Nesfield), which had only been completed some fifty years before. The house had been severely damaged by fire in 1928 and the acquisition report stated that it was in a dangerous condition and in need of demolition. It was thought that 785 acres out of the total of 935 could be successfully planted and that a further 140 were suitable for agricultural use.

The acquisition reports made in the 1920s make it very clear that the estates being purchased were, without exception, in a very run-down condition. That for Croxton Park, for example, drawn up in 1929, described the estate as `partly heath and partly low grade light arable or pasture land which has passed, or is about to pass, out of cultivation'. Feltwell Hall, when investigated prior to purchase, was found to consist almost entirely of heath land, divided here and there by narrow belts of Scots pine, which had formerly sheltered arable fields. On the Downham Hall estate things were particularly bad, to judge from the report of 1923. The property had been subjected to the attentions of the Board of Trade Timber Supply Department during the War, and had subsequently fallen into the hands of speculators. It was described as a `wilderness'. Not a single farm was let or occupied, and no land was being cultivated. `The various land and timber speculators through whose hands these lands have passed during the past 7 years are responsible for the deplorable condition of the estate.' The mansion was untenanted and in disrepair, and all timber of any value had been felled.

In consequence of the timber operations the park, as such, has ceased to exist. An avenue of limes and a few quasi-ornamental trees of little commercial value are all that are left, except in some of the wild belts where a few ragged conifers remain, the best timber having been cut out.

Indeed, even on those estates on which the worst effects of the agricultural depression had been avoided, the timber was generally in a poor condition. At Didlington, for example, the 1924 acquisition report stated that all the belts, clumps and plantations were heavily thinned or poorly stocked. Landed families, or the property speculators who had purchased the estates from them as recession deepened, had been cashing in on their assets in a big way. In addition, all the acquisition reports suggest that the entire area was heavily infested with rabbits, and also that many of the river valleys had become badly water-logged, due to the failure to dredge watercourses regularly or to maintain drainage channels. All in all, this was a landscape in a state of chronic decline.

Not all the land acquired by the Commission in the 1920s and early 30s was purchased freehold. In the early years leases were sometimes preferred. These could be for terms as short as 120 years, enough time to obtain two successive crops of timber, but were often for as much as 999 years. Some of the leased areas were extensive: no less than 4,475 acres (1,811 hectares) were held from the Croxton estate before it was finally purchased, while 552 were leased from the Smith family of the Didlington Hall estate in 1925, and a further 1,588 acres (643 hectares) in 1927 (this land was again eventually bought outright, although not until the 1950s). Extensive areas of Cockley Cley estate were also originally leased, before being purchased: large areas of Lord Iveagh's Elveden estate were acquired in this way, and never actually bought. Like the prices paid for freehold land, the rents paid by the Commission for these properties were very low. The average per annum seems to have been around 2s 9d per acre.

The majority of the land within the main Thetford/Swaffham area of the forest was acquired between 1923 and 1929 - a relatively short time in which to accomplish the effective transfer of some 40,000 acres (1618 hectares). The financial stringencies which had delayed and complicated the acquisition of the Croxton estate in 1929 continued and intensified, with the Committee on National Expenditure even recommending in 1931 that no more land should be acquired by the Commission anywhere in Britain. But by 1934 the Commission's financial position had once again improved and attention now turned to the area to the south of Thetford, and to the acquisition of the area which was to become King's Forest, with the purchase of the Culford Estate in 1934.

Culford appears to have been in a rather better condition than most of the estates bought in the previous decade. Although, like them, it had been managed principally for sport rather than for agriculture or silviculture, the estate was not in an excessively derelict condition. In particular, it contained much flourishing woodland. There were some 150 acres (60 hectares) of belts, mostly consisting of Scots pines some 70-80 years old; 267 acres of mature woods and plantations, mainly of oak and Scots pine, which were in tolerably good condition; and a further 440 acres of immature woodland. The Commission valued the entire estate - 6,900 acres (2,550 hectares) of land, the timber, the sporting rights, and all the estate buildings - at £30,088, or around £4 7s per acre. They offered the vendor £28,200.

The acquisition of Culford was followed, later in 1934, by the purchase of the Mildenhall estate from J.W. Norton. Two years later the Brandon estate to the west of Thetford was acquired. These were the last substantial additions to the main block of Thetford Chase. Both these estates were again in a slightly better condition than the original purchases of the 1920s. Brandon for example, although somewhat run down, contained numerous patches of good-quality naturally-regenerating Scots pine, already 20-30 feet (c.6-10 metres) high. Further purchases augmented the Commission's holdings, and by 1939 it held a total of 59,000 acres (23,000 hectares) in Breckland, of which over three quarters was owned freehold and the rest leased. There have been no further acquisitions of any significance since that time. On the contrary, as we shall see, in the post-War period the Commission were obliged to alienate some of its property in Breckland.

7. Downham Hall, Santon Downham. The house was demolished in 1927 and systematically stripped for building materials by the Forestry Commission.

Managing the Estate

When the Commission purchased their main Breckland properties in the 1920s and 30s they not only acquired land suitable for afforestation but also all the usual components of great estate landscapes - mansion houses, standing timber, parkland, farms, and cottages. The Commission was thus faced with a host of estate management decisions, many of which had little or nothing to do with its primary role, that of planting and managing timber. The problems and the possibilities varied with each individual estate.

The existing timber on the estate was maintained, if not yet mature and in good condition. Otherwise, arrangements were made with local timber merchants (usually Messrs Calders of Thetford) to have it felled and removed. Much of the smaller timber was, however, urgently needed by the Commission itself, especially for the construction of rabbit-proof fences, of which many miles were required as afforestation proceeded. The farms and cottages were sometimes sold off, but often retained as housing for forest workers. The fate of the great mansion houses themselves varied considerably. Downham Hall was already in a fairly run-down state, having been taken over by the military during the First World War, and subsequently used by the Canadian Forestry Core, and for housing German prisoners of war (Figure 7). The Commission was unable to find a suitable buyer and in 1927 the hall was demolished: the costs of this operation were paid for by selling the lead salvaged from the roof. Indeed, the whole building was systematically cannibalised with timber, slates, bricks, even doors and windows being carefully salvaged for future use by the Commission. Lynford Hall had a more complex history. When the Commission purchased the second portion of the Lynford estate in 1929, the building was a fire-damaged shell, in a dangerous condition. The following year the entrepreneur Sir James Calder bought the contents of the kitchen garden and all the garden ornaments and entered into negotiations to lease the remains of the house, together with its gardens and pleasure grounds. The Commission were initially keen to demolish the building down to first floor level but a lease with Calder was finally agreed. He restored the hall, which was eventually returned to the Commission when the lease expired after the Second World War. In 1947 it became one of the Commission's training schools (but was sold off in the 1960s) (Figure 8).

8. Lynford Hall, the magnificent mansion built in the 1850s for Mr Lyne Stephens, 'the richest commoner in England'. It was designed by the architect William Burn: the gardens were by William Andrews Nesfield. (Derek Edwards, Norfolk Landscape Archaeology)

The Commission inherited many of the old staff, and some of the paternalistic responsibilities, of the great estates. The transition was not always a smooth one. At Lynford, for example, the former head gardener, Reid, and his wife refused to vacate a tied cottage when Calder took over the lease of the hall. Reid was now employed by the Forestry Commission but they had not yet supplied him with alternative accommodation. A letter written in June 1930 from the Lynford estate office notes that Reid

> *Although a good workman is a bad tenant, hence my refusal in his application for a cottage. Without a doubt Sir James Calder will want the use of this cottage as soon as he takes possession ... I understand unofficially that Reid is leaving the place in a very bad condition and moreover has been suspected of pilfering from the gardens ...*

By September he had been rehoused in a cottage on the Mundford Road.

When estates were purchased freehold the Commission usually acquired valuable sporting rights, which they were keen to exploit commercially. As early as 1926, those on the Santon Downham estate were bringing in £341 per annum. The good thing about sporting income was that it was not drastically lessened, but was in some cases actually increased, by afforestation. In the late 1950s it was estimated that the income from nearly 60 sporting leases was equivalent to the Commission's entire yearly expenditure on fire control. Arthur Cadman recalled the time in the 1930s when he first worked in the forest:

> *Even in my day at Thetford the sporting rents had gone up to 4s 6d an acre so ... there was a handsome profit from sporting alone, never mind the trees ... Sir James Calder killed a thousand pheasants every year and they were all wild birds. Practically no rearing: there was no need.*

One of the main reasons why some owners preferred to lease their land to the Commission, rather than sell it outright, was that they could thereby retain sporting and a variety of other rights over it. These retentions might, however, interfere in a variety of ways with the Commission's activities, and often involved its representatives in difficult negotiations. Thus Colonel Smith, the owner of the Didlington estate, was reported in April 1925 to be:

> *A bit concerned about gates. Your men told him there would only be slip rails and wire, and as this part of the property is one of his favourite rides (and he is somewhat portly to get up and down!), he hopes very much you will be able to put gates there, that he can open on horseback.*

Colonel Smith also wanted the Commission to leave unplanted shooting rides through his property, 40 yards (c.40 metres) wide, running roughly east-west and spaced c.300 yards (c.300 metres) apart, together with subsidiary rides running at right angles, which were to be around 60 feet wide. For a variety of reasons, the Commission would not agree to this, insisting instead that the Colonel should be content with a more modest layout, consisting of only two parallel rides (with the neighbouring road making a third). These were to be maintained by the Commission, and in August the Divisional Officer wrote that:

> *I find it is far too expensive to employ a tractor for re-ploughing or harrowing the rides. The best method is to use a strong horse with a weighted harrow and churn the ploughed ride well up.*

Such relics of a bygone age might live on for a time, and the Commission clearly did assume some of the roles of a traditional landed estate. But it is nevertheless hard to over-estimate the scale of the changes made to the structure of local society by the steady growth of the Forestry Commission's holdings during the 1920s and 30s. A landscape dominated by vast and decaying estates had, over large parts of the region, been acquired by a young and vigorous institution with a very different agenda. By 1935 the Commission was the largest landowner in East Anglia: and the landscape of Breckland was already being transformed.

Chapter 3

Establishing the Forest: the Inter-War Years

Chapter 3. Establishing the Forest: the Inter-War Years

Almost as soon as a property was acquired by the Commission, planting began. Once again, it is hard to exaggerate the scale of the transformation. The average planting rate in Breckland during the period 1922-1960 was around 1,300 acres (c.526 hectares) per year: but the overwhelming majority of the forest was planted within the first twenty years, and the bulk of this in the first decade. The number of trees planted increased steadily through the 1920s, peaking in 1927, when no less than eight million were planted on 3,700 acres in Thetford `Chase', as the area of plantations around Thetford was originally known, with a further 700 acres being planted up in the area around Swaffham. Between 1924 and 1929, an average of 2,226 acres (909 hectares) was planted annually. After 1931 there was a sure, if gradual, decline in the rate of planting, as the number of new land acquisitions dwindled and as the available acreage was afforested. The establishment of King's Forest from 1935 in the area to the south of Thetford increased the local amount of planting, but not to any significant extent the overall total in the region, for King's occupied only around 6,000 acres (2,430 hectares), compared with the 52,000 covered by the combined area of the Thetford and Swaffham Forests. This limited area was soon planted up. By 1945 no trees at all were being planted in Swaffham or King's, and only limited areas of new planting were being established in Thetford: planting was at its lowest level since 1922. This slow-down was partly due to the effects of the War, but mainly reflected the simple fact that most of the available land owned by the Commission had now been planted. With the return of peace in 1945 the amount of new planting carried out each year gradually increased once more, although it remained at relatively low levels until the mid-1960s, since when it has increased steadily, as the original trees have been felled and large-scale restocking has commenced.

Foresters and Others

Who were the people responsible for the great transformation of the landscape in the inter-War years, and how was this enterprise managed? The administrative organisation of the forest has changed on a number of occasions. The three main areas of the Forest - that is, the distinct blocks of Thetford Chase, Swaffham Forest and King's Forest - were subdivided into units called *beats*. The pattern of these units changed over time, as they subdivided, amalgamated, and changed their names in complex ways. Originally there were only two, Broomhouse and Downham, but their numbers increased steadily during the inter-war years to reach a peak of 16. This expansion reflected both the steady growth in the size of the forest, and also to some extent in the number of people working within it.

To begin with, most decisions effecting the Breckland forests were taken locally: administration was based at the Divisional Office at Santon Downham. After 1928, however, control over all the Forestry Commission's Eastern Division (its holdings in East Anglia and adjacent regions) was centralised at Cambridge. At a local level, authority rested with the Divisional or District Officers: below them were the *Foresters*, distinguished from the other forest workers by the regularity and continuity of their employment, and also by the extent of their training, which over time became longer and more sophisticated. By the 1940s they usually trained for two years in one of the Commission's Forestry Schools. Beneath the foresters were the *Gangers,* or foremen. They supervised the activities of the *Forest Workers,* who were normally organised into gangs of between three and thirty, depending on the task at hand. Most of their work - clearing ground, planting, weeding, and later brashing and thinning - was carried out at piece rates, common practice with agricultural work at this time. Many were employed periodically, or on a part-time basis.

The foresters were often recruited from the ranks of the forest workers, so even in the 1920s and 30s there was a degree of upward mobility in the Commission. But only within limits. It was rare for a forester to rise to the level of District Officer. As Arthur Cadman, who was a probationary District Officer in the forest in the 1930s, later recalled: `A District Officer had to have a degree in one of the four universities - that is, Oxford, Edinburgh, Bangor, and Aberdeen - that did a forestry course'. But the distinction between Officers and the rest was not simply a matter of education: it was also a matter of class and background. It was a distinction analogous, in Cadman's words, to that between `NCOs and Officers in the army'. Most District Officers were recruited from affluent country families. Younger sons of landowners, in particular, were attracted to this new profession at a time when, for the most part, agriculture was in a state of depression. Arthur Cadman recalled how he himself came into the Forestry service:

My father was a landowner who farmed some of his farms himself. I wanted to be a farmer and of course, I was ready to be trained. During the 1930s slump, when my father retired finally, he said `you can't take up farming, there is nothing in it'. So I looked around for another outdoor job and forestry in those days was the only alternative in Britain, a new thing. And so he very kindly sent me to University and that's why I started in forestry ... I think District Officers were largely recruited from the big families in the country: landowners and so on.

The Choice of Pine

When planting began in the 1920s the Commission's initial choice as the main forest tree for the Breckland area was Scots pine. There were a number of reasons why this particular species was selected. Given the adverse local conditions of soil and climate, the Commission was eager to use a species which had a proven track record in Breckland, and one for which seeds were readily available in the locality. The Scots pine was already widely established in the area both as a plantation tree and also, as we have seen, as a hedging plant. It can, indeed, be grown successfully and established easily on almost all sites within the forest. Yet although it was the main tree planted in the early years, Scots pine was never the only species used by the Commission. Corsican pine, in particular, was being established at certain locations from the early 1920s. It is now the dominant tree in Breckland, but was originally less favoured than the Scots pine. This was because it was less easy to obtain large quantities of its seed; it was less easy to germinate from seed; and once germinated, it was rather more difficult to establish, especially in open situations. In addition, there seems to have been a certain reluctance to choose a tree which was at the time not as familiar to timber merchants as the indigenous pine.

Douglas fir and European larch were also planted in a number of locations during the 1920s, but were soon found to be less tolerant of local conditions than the pines. These species tended to survive and prosper only in areas which were relatively free from unseasonable frosts: elsewhere they failed, and had to be replaced. During the 1930s various other species were tried out, partly on an experimental basis. Serbian spruce and silver fir were established in a few places and, on a very small scale, stands of Lawson's cypress, western red cedar, and western hemlock. In the 1940s and 1950s, experiments were made with growing maritime and lodgepole pines, Austrian pines, Monterrey pines, five-needled pines, Western white pine, and Weymouth pine, but none were established on a very wide scale.

What is perhaps surprising is that substantial numbers of indigenous hardwood trees were also planted in the forest during the 1920s and 30s: rather more than the present make-up of the forest would appear to suggest, although they were always greatly outnumbered by pines. In 1927, for example, no less than 487 acres (197 hectares) were planted with broadleaved trees, although more than seven times this area (3,436 acres, 1390 hectares) was planted with conifers. During subsequent years, the proportion of deciduous trees planted was generally much lower, although by no means negligible. The highest ratio came in the following decade, in 1935, when 1,186 acres (480 hectares) of conifers were planted to 428 of hardwood trees. Beech was the most widely planted hardwood. It was principally established on the more calcareous soils within the forest where it was usually well mixed with `nurses' of pine or larch. It was especially prominent in the area around Harling. Oak was also fairly widely planted on some of the better, loamier soils in the eastern parts of the forest, around Hockham, Roudham, and Harling, again mixed with larch and pine. One and a half million were planted in Thetford Chase in 1931, although this was very exceptional: in all other years the number was less than 300,000.

In the 1920s and early 30s some people believed that the proportion of hardwoods would increase, and that they would eventually come to dominate the forest, after the first fellings of pine had allowed the soil conditions in the area to improve. It soon became apparent, however, that this minority view was untenable. The main problem with both oak and beech was their vulnerability to spring frosts. Deer were also a threat, particularly to beech. They stripped the bark from the young trees, and browsed off the spring foliage. Once they had grown above the level of the early summer air frosts beech did quite well on the less acid soils, but its high initial failure rate soon rendered it unpopular as a major component of the forest. Around 50% of the beeches planted on the Elveden beat were lost in the first few years, and had to be replaced with other trees, at considerable expense. Oaks tended to fare better, especially in the early years of growth. But they grew slowly compared with pines, and were increasingly considered uneconomic. The numbers being planted declined after 1935, and the Working Plan of 1959 concluded that the species would have little place in the future development of the forest.

Beech continued to be planted on a moderate scale as a commercial crop, a variety of poplars was established on the fen soils, ash was planted in some areas, and birch widely used as a nurse (it is the only broadleaf tree which establishes itself with relative ease on open heaths). But the most significant impact made by hardwoods in the forest was in the form of narrow roadside belts which, as discussed below, were mainly established as a fire control measure. A wide variety of hardwood species can be found in these, including - besides oak and beech - lime, walnut, red oak, and Norway maple (these trees seem to do well enough, perhaps because their proximity to roads, and therefore traffic, discouraged deer and thus reduced one of the principal threats to hardwoods in Breckland). Other limited stands of hardwoods were planted for particular reasons. In King's Forest a special plantation, in the form of a crown was established in 1937 to commemorate the coronation of George V, together with a long avenue of beeches - Queen Mary's Avenue (similar commemorative plantations were established at the same time in other British forests).

Both environmental constraints and economic considerations thus ensured that not only oak and beech, but also fir, larch and most other conifers, were only ever planted on a very limited scale in the forest. From first to last, pine predominated. Yet there was a gradual change in the most favoured species. By 1940 the amount of Corsican pine being planted was steadily increasing relative to Scots. There were a number of reasons for this. Although the Scots pine was, for the most part, easier to establish in Breckland's hostile environment than the Corsican, the latter produced a higher volume of timber per acre, had a better stem form, a greater tolerance of the thinner, more chalky soils, and a greater resistance to fungal diseases and insect pests. By the 1950s Scots pine was being chosen as the main crop only for the very best soils, or for pronounced frost hollows in which Corsican pine would be exceptionally difficult to establish. Nevertheless, as the first clear fellings got under way in the 1960s the forest was still composed predominantly of Scots pine. The Working Plan Report of 1966 estimated that 54% of the Commission's 70 square miles of plantations were composed of Scots pine; 21% of Corsican; 2% of Douglas fir; 8% of other conifers; 4% of mixed conifers and broadleaves; and only 11% of broadleaves alone, mostly in roadside belts.

Planting

The vast quantities of trees needed for the forest in the 1920s and 30s required huge amounts of seed. In the early years some of the seed was brought in from outside the area but most was obtained locally. Men and women were sent out into the countryside, gathering cones from old plantations, and also from the pine hedges and rows bordering the fields. Only as the plantations matured was it possible to gather seeds from the forest itself. From 1925 the seeds were extracted from cones at the Seed Extraction Plant, which was located at Santon Downham: this continued to operate until 1964, when all Forestry Commission seed extraction in southern England was centralised at Alice Holt in Hampshire. The Santon plant was modified

9. Examining seeds at the Santon Downham Seed Extraction Plant in the 1940s.

on several occasions but the operating principal remained the same. The green cones were stacked in wire trays over hot water pipes, which were initially heated by four coke boilers, later by two, supplemented by electricity. The heat caused the cones to open, and the small winged seeds to drop out. These were then collected up, cleaned, and stored in airtight jars until needed (Figure 9). From a bushel of cones, it was possible to extract about half a pound of seed. This does not sound like a vast amount, until it is remembered that there are about 7,000 Scots pine seeds to the lb. Indeed, by the 1940s so many seeds were being produced at Santon Downham that a surplus was available for sale: pines from Thetford now grow in the USA and South Africa.

The seeds were taken to a nursery and set in seed beds 3 feet wide, separated by paths 18 inches in width. To begin with the usual practise was to plant the seeds very densely: about lb of seeds were sown to every 100 square yards. Billy Steel, who worked in the Santon nursery during the 1920s, remembered how the seed-bed was prepared with a small hand roller, made out of a piece of pine or larch timber, and ribbed so that a number of drill lines were made in the seed bed. The seed was then shaken into these using a small container - such as an old cocoa tin - with holes cut into the base. From around 1930, however, this method was changed. It was discovered that better results could be obtained by sowing the seed broadcast - that is, scattering it randomly and evenly - rather than planting it in lines. This allowed each tree to stand singly in the seed bed, whereas the original method had tended to make the plants grow rather densely crowded. The new method also had disadvantages, however. In particular it was more difficult to keep the ground clear of weeds. Chemical weedkillers had not yet been invented and so it was necessary to hoe between the seedlings with small hand hoes - an operation which was, for obvious reasons, rather easier to perform when the plants were growing in neat rows. Nevertheless, the broadcast method was adopted because it did produce better results, in the form of faster and firmer growth in the young plants.

In the 1920s the seedlings were transplanted after only one year's growth, but later, in the 1930s, this period was lengthened to two years. It was always known that the latter method produced stronger plants but it could not be adopted in the early years because of the need to produce vast numbers of young trees very quickly. The seedlings were lifted with a knife: the work was paid at piece rates, 4d a hundred in the early days of the nursery. Bill Steel remembered that he was one of the fastest at pulling them up: 30,000 a day (`there wasn't many people who could catch you up at that').

Today, container-grown seedlings are often planted out directly in the forest, but partly because of problems of weed control this was never the practice in the 1920s and 30s, or even the 40s and 50s. Instead the young plants were `lined out' in nurseries, that is, placed in rows about 2 inches apart and allowed to grow for one, sometimes two years, in order to gain greater height and more substantial and fibrous roots (Figure 10).

10. Young Scots pines 'lined out' in the Santon Downham nursery in 1949

The development of nurseries in the forest was complex, and is poorly documented. The earliest were at Santon Downham, which was mainly used to produce seedlings; and at Lynford, a larger establishment of around 100 acres (40 hectares), which was mainly used for `lining out'. As the forest expanded during the 1920s, a number of others were established at strategic locations, including West Harling, Roudham, and Swaffham (where there were two). When planting was at its height, there were some 200 acres (80 hectares) of nursery scattered around the forest, producing around seven million transplants per year.

After the trees had been lined out for one or two years they were taken out of the nursery and planted in the forest. Before this could happen, however, a considerable amount of work had to go into preparing the ground. In some areas of derelict land fairly thick vegetation - bracken, heather, and stands of rose bay willowherb - had to be cleared by hand. Once this had been accomplished the area had to be securely fenced against attacks from the ubiquitous rabbits. As much as 700 acres (c.280 hectares) at a time might be enclosed with rabbit-proof fencing. Enclosure on this scale not only required many miles of wire netting, but also many hundreds of fencing posts which were, in the early days, often supplied from the smaller timber growing in existing estate woodlands acquired by the Commission. Once an area had been fenced, all the rabbits within it were killed or driven out - a task carried out by gangs of warreners employed directly by the Commission. The warreners normally used the traditional long nets, which had been used for centuries on the Breckland warrens: a method which could not be employed so easily once the forest was planted, because it required extensive open spaces. The nets were about three feet high, with a very fine mesh. Rex Witta recalled seeing the warreners in action:

11. Scots pines ready for planting, c.1940.

And then they used to put wings on them, and they used to get a group of men, they used to walk the piece towards the net and the hares and rabbits would go into the net. If it was going well, it was worth watching.

Thirty or forty rabbits would be caught each time and the operation - together with other forms of trapping - was repeated over and over again. At Santon Downham, throughout most of 1923, 500 rabbits were killed each week at a cost of 4d per rabbit: but the rabbits were sold for 1s each to the Brandon furriers, and the Commission thus made a tidy profit of around £15 per week, amounting to more than £500 over the year.

Once the rabbits had been eliminated the area within the fenced block was ready for ploughing. In the early days of the forest this was usually carried out using contract labour. Horses were initially employed to pull the ploughs, although

12. Planting Scots pines by hand: this undated photograph, probably taken in the late 1930s, gives a good impression of the hard and tedious work that went into creating the forest.

tractors began to come into operation during the 1930s. Originally, in the 1920s, a single mouldboard plough was used to make furrows which were spaced at intervals of 4½ feet. Later, in the 1930s, when King's Forest was established, a more specialised form of plough was adopted. This cut two parallel furrows spaced at the correct planting distance. Later still, during the 1939-45 War, a yet more advanced plough was developed which cut a deeper furrow, and which laid the turf neatly on each side of the line, thus helping to suppress weed growth.

After the area had been ploughed men walked down the furrows, placing the transplants in small spade-dug holes. They carried the young trees in bags

13. Scots pines established on open heathland somewhere in Thetford forest. This undated photograph from the 1930s vividly conveys the open, empty nature of much of the Breckland landscape before afforestation.

hanging across their backs (Figure 12). The holes were spaced at regular intervals of 4½ feet which, as the furrows themselves had the same spacing, gave an overall planting density of about 2,100 trees per acre (c.5,190 per hectare) (Figure 13). Such dense planting was intended to ensure the rapid upward growth of the trees, as they competed with each other, searching upwards for the light. It also, after a while, provided a canopy dense enough to kill off competing vegetation.

The planted areas were divided into blocks called compartments, each of about twenty or thirty acres (12 hectares). These were separated from each other by rides, often 30 feet (c. 10 metres) in width, which provided access and a measure of fire protection. The pattern of rides and compartment boundaries was not entirely new: many developed from earlier trackways and field boundaries. As Figure 14 shows, there was much more continuity between the old landscape, and the new, than is often assumed.

Each compartment had, and usually still has, an identifying number displayed at the corners, on a plate or painted on a tree. Once planted a new compartment had to be regularly maintained during the first few years of growth. In particular, until the trees reached six or more feet, and lateral growth began to shade out other plants, they had to be protected from the smothering effects of weeds. Gangs of men were sent during the summer to `clean' the plantations, cutting down the grasses, bracken, and other plants with reap hooks and sickles. This could be a dangerous job, for when the bracken was high a man might inadvertently swing his sickle too far to either side and cut the legs of the man working in the next row. This

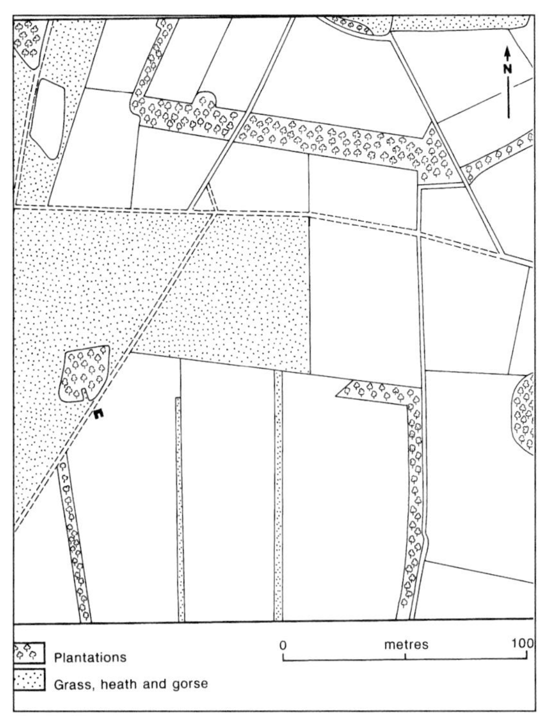

14. (a) An area to the south of Cranwich before afforestation: the pattern of land use shown is that depicted on the Tithe Award map of 1845. Note the scatter of small plantation, and the limited extent of surviving heathland. The unshaded areas are arable fields or arable 'breaks'.

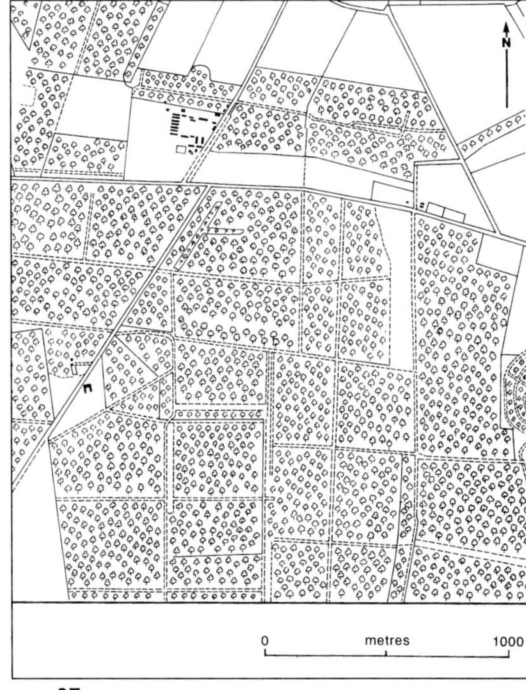

14. (b) The same area following afforestation. Note the extent to which the principal rides and compartment boundaries follow the lines of earlier features in the landscape.

problem was eventually solved by the simple expedient of getting the workers to cut every other row, each man taking responsibility for two rows at a time, cutting up one and then down the other, and working in staggered lines.

Not all the trees planted in a compartment necessarily survived, and so planting was followed by the process of `beating up' - that is, the replacement of any trees which had died within the first two or three years of growth. This was a particularly important activity because gaps in the plantation would lead to uneven, and deformed, growth in the adjacent trees. The thoroughness with which `beating up' was carried out varied over the years, however, depending on the amount of money and labour available, and the quantity of planting being carried out.

Establishing the forest was an incredible achievement, especially when it is remembered that almost all the tasks were carried out by hand. Planting the individual trees was particularly cold and uncomfortable work for it largely took place in the winter months, and certainly before the buds began to form in April. Like all the tasks so far described, it was done at piece rates, and low ones at that. During the 1920s, the normal rate was 6d for every 100 trees planted. A good man could plant as many 1,500 in a day and earn 7s 6d, the task being considerably aided by the fact that it was relatively easy to dig holes in the light Breckland soils (except when the ground was frozen hard, in which case a mattock had to be used, reducing the planting speed by about a third). But even so, this was no very princely sum, and low labour costs were the main reason why the initial planting of the forest was carried out so cheaply: the entire cost of planting in the 1920s - inclusive of fencing, clearing and ploughing the land, killing rabbits, and the cost of the plants - was usually no more than £4 10s (£4.50) per acre.

Labour and Labour Camps

Although the conditions might be hard and the pay low the Commission had no problem recruiting workers in the 1920s and 30s. The general shortage of employment opportunities in the area had recently been made worse by the closure of one of the main industrial employers, Burrell's, the steam traction-engine manufacturers at Thetford. The Forestry Commission, right from its initial inception, was always considered to have an important social role: its advocates argued that it would help alleviate unemployment in remote, depressed regions of rural Britain. Areas like the Breckland could not only provide a large amount of cheap and under-utilised land, but also a pool of cheap and under-utilised labour. That the latter was seen as a positive advantage when the forest was first being mooted is clear from many of the Acquisition Reports. The Report for the Santon Downham estate, for example, stated that one of the advantages of the purchase was the fact that there were between 600 and 700 unemployed men in the area. The only problem was that few of these had any experience of forest work, in spite of the presence of some estate woodland in the area. The establishment of the forest clearly made an impact on local unemployment, and people were keen to take up forestry work, especially as the job came with a house: old estate cottages or, a little later, small bungalows. Many of these, moreover, had a smallholding attached - usually four or five acres (two hectares) of land in the early years, but later sometimes ten or more.

The provision of smallholdings was a policy adopted in most parts of Britain in which the Commission established plantations. It made sound economic sense in a number of ways. Together with poor land suitable for afforestation, the Commission often acquired, when it purchased estates, some better-quality land suitable for small-scale agricultural concerns. More important was the fact that in the early years, in particular, much of the Commission's demand for labour was seasonal. In the case of the Breckland smallholdings, the Commission guaranteed 150 days work per year: and charged a rent on the capital value of the property. The occupants had also, by the terms of the lease, to perform a number of other duties, keeping a general eye on the Commission's large and expanding domain. They had, as far as possible, to keep a watch over and protect Forestry Commission property in the vicinity of their holding; they had to `exterminate and keep exterminated all rabbits, hares and vermin'; and they were to use their `utmost endeavours to preserve the game and eggs and young of game from being injured or destroyed'. Partly for this reason, but also because some of the houses had formerly been estate cottages, the smallholdings were quite widely scattered through the forests, although there were some sizeable concentrations, like that at Drymere near Swaffham, on the Beechamwell Road, which is still a noticeable feature of the landscape. The new bungalows were built by direct Commission labour. Their roofs were of timber and asbestos slates, their walls usually of brick, much of it salvaged from the demolition of Downham Hall and other redundant estate buildings. By 1926 there were already 120 smallholdings in the forest, and a co-operative marketing scheme had been established. Poultry, eggs, and honey were sent `direct to the consumers in London at prices lower than those prevailing there but considerably better than can be obtained locally'. In the later 1920s, some of the forest holdings were used to house unemployed people, mainly miners, from the depressed areas of northern England - a good example of the social role adopted by, or thrust upon, the Commission. The recruits were given assistance with stocking, and provided with some basic training.

It was, needless to say, not easy to make a living on this poor land, even though the holdings were, as noted above, usually located on the better soils within the forest. Graham Hobbs recalled how:

They went into blackcurrants and asparagus, things like that, you know a little bit of corn and that, built a pigsty. What happened with a lot of them was that they had a horse and very often the Forestry Commission would employ that horse, ploughing for planting and things like that. I suppose it was a good idea at the time.

But few of the smallholdings proved very successful in the long run. Billy Steel believed that those resettled from the north had the greatest difficulty.

I don't think they had the experience of course, being miners. They came out of the cities, or the depressed areas. A local man did best, probably. We've got one or two who made a go of it.

But the depression of the 1920s and 30s saw the Forest used in a more radical way as a means of dealing with the unemployed: as Billy Steel recalled, `... the main work creation scheme was in the depression, 1928 and right up to the War. There were the labour camps about here'. These were the local manifestation of a more extensive national scheme, run by the Ministry of Labour but using land supplied by the Forestry Commission. By 1938, there were 21 camps and a further 10 used only during the summer months, scattered through the nation's infant forests. By this date they housed, in all, nearly 6,000 men.

When first established in 1928, the camps had been used for training men for overseas colonial settlement, providing instruction in land-clearance, drainage, fencing, etc. But within a year they had a simpler function. The overseas training element was dropped: the camps were now expressly intended for:

A class of men to whom our existing training schemes do not apply. I refer to those, especially among the younger men, who through prolonged unemployment have become so `soft' and temporarily demoralised [that they are a] danger to the morale of the ordinary training centres ... and ... cannot be considered for transfer until they are hardened.

Originally described as `Hardening Centres', later as `Transfer Instructional Centres', to most people they were simply the Labour Camps; and to the National Unemployed Workers Union they were the Slave Camps. Four of these institutions were established by the Ministry of Labour within Breckland: at West Tofts, High Lodge, Cranwich, and Weeting. The Weeting camp made use of the redundant Weeting hall. The others were purpose-built collections of huts, rather like army camps.

The camps were supposed to provide work of `sufficient utility to have some interest for the men'.

The course of instruction takes the form of giving the trainees work such as road-making, scrub-clearing, etc., which will ultimately prove useful in working the forests but would not normally be undertaken for some years to come. There is consequently no displacement of local labour.

The isolated locations of the Forestry Commission estates - both here and in the Welsh uplands, where most of the other camps were established - was considered an advantage by proponents of the scheme, because it kept the men away from the `depressing atmosphere' of areas badly effected by the slump. The camps were run on strict disciplinarian lines, and the camp manager was usually an ex-soldier. Men generally attended for a maximum of twelve weeks. To begin with, the camps only took men for whom subsequent employment or further training could be arranged. But later, as the depression deepened, jobs were only given to the more conscientious trainees, and used in effect as a tool, to maintain camp discipline. From 1934, anyone claiming National Insurance had to attend a camp if required to do so, or lose their benefit. Compulsory attendance was actually sanctioned by Parliamentary act although never brought in. The `trainees' retained only 4s of their benefit: in 1934 this was reduced to 1s. The rest was taken for board and lodging. There was some compensation for this in the provision of free boots, overall, oilskins, etc., which could be retained by the (minority) who stayed the full three months.

Graham Hobbs recalled how the labour camps were occupied by people who were:

Mainly down from the north. A lot were Geordies, from industrial areas and that, who were out of work. And they paid them something ... kept them in a pair of cords and a jacket and whatnot, and food: and they did a lot of work in the forest, mainly making forest roads, by hand. I remember going round with my father and seeing these gangs. Most of them ended up in the army ... They were just a work creation scheme.

They were indeed: on the rare occasions when work of `sufficient utility' was unavailable, pointless tasks might be thought up. One twenty-year-old at High Lodge reputedly spent three months digging trenches and filling them in again. The rough and isolated conditions could have violent and tragic consequences: there was at least one serious riot, at High Lodge, and one suicide, at Brandon. New arrivals at the camps were greeted with shouts of `you'll never get out'. Perhaps more would be known about this darker side of the forest's history if the files relating to the camps had not been `destroyed by fire' at the outbreak of the War. What we do know about life in the camps comes, in the main, from personal memories. One inmate, Walter Wild, recalled his time at West Tofts camp:

It was very rough, very rough; conditions of sleeping and all that. They were really tough guys. Biggest part of them were seamen, trawler men that had become unemployed, you know, really tough guys ... They'd get fighting at times, you know, among themselves ... The manager was an ex-army officer, you know, he'd got those highly polished officer boots and a clipped moustache, sort of stuff ... You had to be prompt on parade and things like that. We didn't seem to come into contact with [Forestry Commission] staff other than Gangers. We seemed to be herded together in these huts all the time. It was miles out.

It is possible that some of the Camps' occupants found them a welcome change from their homes in the depressed areas of the North and West: no worse than tramping the streets, looking for non-existent work. And the camps did provide some rudimentary education in gardening, joinery, etc. But they mainly supplied cheap labour for the Commission. Road making (clearing dirt tracks in the forest) was perhaps their main activity, but the gangs performed a variety of other tasks, after being picked up by lorry in the morning from the camps. They cleared the forest rides and scoured the drainage channels to reclaim derelict meadow land in the river valleys. Their activities in the latter area were not always successful. In 1939 one landowner complained that flooding on his land was due to the destruction of a dam and a sluice on Commission property. `The foundations of these were taken out when men from the Cranwich camp cleared it out and the bricks were carted away'. The Ministry of Labour, which ran the camps, provided the gangs with pickaxes, spades, mattocks and other tools: the Commission provided larger things, like wheelbarrows and planks.

Various scraps of information suggest that the attitude of the Commission's administrators and workers towards the labour gangs was somewhat more humane than that of the Ministry of Labour's officials responsible for running the camps. Certainly, the Commission was uneasy about using the gangs for some tasks. When the demolition of Lynford Hall was being mooted in 1930 it was suggested that `As the men will be irresponsible ... it would be highly dangerous to put them on demolition of the ruins of the hall'. Walter Wild recalled an incident when a gang mutinied:

It was pouring with rain, see. We packed in. We said: `We are not working in the rain'. He [the Ganger] says `Come on, get in ...' `Look', I says, `You get three pound a week, we only get three shillings a week ... we're not going to work in the rain for that'. He climbed down a bit and said `I can see your point of view'.

The trainees had little to do during their leisure time. The camps were a long distance from any pub. There was originally a bus running from the camps at West Tofts and Weeting to Brandon but this was discontinued after the conductress was assaulted. Anyone wanting a drink had to walk six miles each way, and be back in the camps by 10.00 pm. Graham Hobbs used to see them in his youth:

They were at a loose end at the weekends. I can remember as a lad seeing these people walking down the roads round about, and they used to go down the pub. Of course, they couldn't afford too much beer and things like that.

The unemployment schemes, and mass unemployment itself, came to an end with the onset of the War in 1939. This created an entirely new employment situation in the forest, as the younger, fitter and more able men in the district left to join the forces, or to take up the various new opportunities opened up by the War.

By this time most of the land in Breckland acquired by the Commission had been planted with trees. It now owned or leased no less than 59,000 acres (nearly 24,000 hectares) of Breckland, of which some 42,000 had been afforested. And so it was that within little more than a decade and a half the landscape of much of Breckland was transformed. The broad outlines of this story, as recorded in a variety of documents and as recalled by people who were involved in this great task, are tolerably clear. What is less clear is the extent to which the Commission had from the start a fully-developed, long-term plan for the forest. In particular, it is not very evident that the problems of subsequent management, especially the question of how to dispose of the thinnings which would soon need to be removed from the plantations, were given a great deal of consideration while planting was under way. This is perhaps understandable given the enormous size of the task being undertaken, and the fact that government enthusiasm for the enterprise was by no means unwavering or overwhelming during the 1920s and 30s. But there does seem to have been a certain amount of confusion over long-term policy and aims, especially at a local level. In particular, many workers seem to have been under the impression that the forest was only going to be a temporary feature. Billy Steel recalled:

> *The whole object was, they told us, that after say 80 years all the Forestry Commission land would be cut down and go back to agriculture, because the pine needles would have gone into the soil and rotted away, and then it'd be better for agriculture. That's what they taught us.*

In reality, of course, the forest was firmly established as a permanent addition to the landscape. Yet much remained to be done, managing and protecting it while it matured. Planting the forest was only the start of the story.

Chapter 4

The Forest Matures

Chapter 4. The Forest Matures

Once the trees had been planted they were not simply left alone to grow to maturity. On the contrary: they had to be managed, in fairly complex ways, in order to ensure that the maximum volume of timber was produced. As already described, the early plantations were planted fairly densely in order to ensure that the trees were established quickly and grew straight and tall. But it was never the intention to allow the timber to mature in such close-packed masses.

15. Branches from thinned trees being loaded onto a cart, c.1940.

Brashing and Thinning

After the trees had been established the first stage in the management process came when they were about 20 feet high and the canopy had closed sufficiently to kill off the lower side branches. This was *brashing*, the removal of all side branches up to a height of around six feet (c.2 metres), using pruning saws, pruning chisels, and billhooks. This was done for a number of reasons: in order to improve the shape and upward growth of the tree, and in particular to ensure that the first six feet of all sawlogs would have only a very small knotty core; to reduce the threat of fire; and to make access to the plantations easier. Brashing was usually carried out during the spring and summer months, and it was often the practice to remove seed cones, green, from the branches, to be sent to the Seed Extraction Plant at Santon Downham. Betty Witta was later to recall her work brashing in the late 1940s:

> *Well, it was always hard work. You see, we didn't have anywhere if it rained. If it rained you got wet ... We used to drag the branches back. The first five rows had to be completely clear. That used to go right throughout the block. And every five rows there used to be a clear one, so the foresters could go down. They called them inspection racks.*

The next stage after brashing was thinning. Originally, a process called *pre-thinning* was carried out when the plantations were 15 or 16 years old: this first occurred in the Swaffham area in 1937. It involved the removal of trees damaged by disease or insect attack, and also of *wolves*: that is, large, dominant trees with spreading branches and crooked or deformed stems, which suppressed their straighter, less dominant but more valuable neighbours. Wolves were sometimes genetically abnormal specimens, but often the consequence of not having `beaten up' a plantation properly in the first few years after planting: if a gap had been left by the death of one or more young trees, the adjacent survivors would tend to grow much larger, and usually less straight, than the others in the plantation. Pre-thinning was abandoned in the following decade, largely because insect-damage became less of a

16. Thinning in Thetford forest, c.1949. The man in the foreground is trimming thinnings with a axe.

problem as attacks by the Pine Shoot moth declined (see below, chapter 5). Instead, `wolves' and other damaged trees were removed during the normal process of thinning.

Thinning began when the trees were 18 to 20 years old (Figure 16). The first plantations in the forest were thus becoming due for attention around the start of the Second World War. At this time there was much debate about how the task should best be carried out. A research programme, the East Anglian Pine Thinning Project, was set up in 1939 `in order to determine the effects of thinning on increment with the object of evolving a suitable thinning policy for Corsican pine and Scots pine plantations in East Anglia'. During the early 1940s a variety of different patterns and densities of removal was examined: the project carefully weighed the benefits of each in terms of the increased growth predicted for the final timber crop, the economic value of the thinned material, and the costs in labour and materials of the thinning procedures themselves.

The system which initially evolved was a simple one. First, `racks' or access ways 18-20 feet (c.6-7 metres) in width were cut, dividing the compartments into blocks each covering c.5 acres (2 hectares). Next, two rows in every thirty were removed to create smaller `racks', each some 10 feet (c.3 metres) wide. After this, the Gangers or foremen moved in and, after some consultation with the foresters, marked the less promising trees for thinning. Then the forest workers began to fell and extract the trees. Including those removed from the racks, the usual abstraction rate at first thinning was around 200-300 trees per acre (500-740 per hectare). Five or so years later, a second thinning was carried out, this time removing some 100-150 trees per acre. This, at least, was the method first developed. In practice, other systems were adopted, often involving only a single phase of thinning. Either way, conifer plantations could be thinned at any time of the year, but hardwoods only during the winter months, when the leaves were off the trees. In contrast to some Forestry Commission plantations elsewhere in Britain, horses do not seem to have been used in

17. High Pruning in Thetford Forest, c.1945. Women workers were extensively used in the forest during the war years.

18. Preparing pit props at Brandon Central Depot in 1949

Breckland for removing the thinned timber. Instead the poles were carried by hand down the racks to the main rides or, later, hauled out using agricultural tractors (usually Fergursons).

In some plantations thinning was accompanied, or followed by, `high pruning': that is, the removal of the higher branches, above the brashed stem, in order to produce a long, knot-free bole (Figure 17). The process could create some 20 feet (6 metres) of high-quality saw timber. Some 200 trees per acre (c.500 per hectare) were selected for this treatment. The incidence of high pruning has varied greatly over the years. Because it was not absolutely essential, the practice tended to take second place to more pressing tasks, and to be carried out in slack periods. It was generally abandoned altogether during times of financial stringency, which the Commission experienced at various stages during the 1940s and 50s, as Government policy towards forestry vacillated. Since the late 1960s it has been abandoned altogether.

At the same time as the need for brashing and thinning was increasing during the 1940s, the amount of new planting was declining to very low levels, and as a result the number of nurseries in the forest was steadily reduced. By 1950, there were only some 72 acres (c.30 hectares) of nursery ground, and by the end of the decade the seven remaining nurseries specialised in particular kinds of tree. Thus the 14-acre (c.6-hectare) nursery at Harling grew much beech, oak, and poplar, because of the chalky nature of the soil; Elveden, which covered around four acres (c.1.6 hectares), grew seedlings and transplants of silver firs, western hemlock, and Lawson's cypress; while the small nursery at Downham specialised in poplars. At High Lodge, seedlings of silver fir, Douglas fir, and Lawson's cypress were raised. Santon, which had originally concentrated on seedlings of Scots pine, now also produced Douglas fir and western hemlock, while King's nursery specialised in transplants of larch, Douglas fir, and beech. The most extensive nursery was that at Roudham, which grew all species of conifer seedlings and transplants required locally, but particularly pines. This was the main nursery, and extended over some 26 acres (10.5 hectares) beside the railway line at Roudham Heath. In 1959 it was described as being `as mechanised as any in the country'. It had ten Fergurson tractors, a fleet of 12 lorries, and a variety of other machinery. In addition to these relatively permanent establishments, a number of small, temporary nurseries existed at this time at various points within the forest. During the 1960s, however, the number of nurseries decreased further, and by the early 1970s most activity was concentrated at Santon Downham and Elveden.

The Thinning Problem

The first clear fellings in Thetford Forest only began in 1963. These were of trees little more than 40 years old: that is, trees which were not yet fully mature. Some of these premature fellings were due to the need to salvage usable timber from plantations damaged by pests or disease, but most were carried out because the forest had been established during a relatively short period of time, so that large areas were coming to maturity (i.e., would be 60 or so years old) at around the same time. The policy adopted ensured that the work of felling, and of replanting the felled areas, could be more evenly spread. But the fellings of the 1960s were on a comparatively small scale, and even in 1975 only around a third of the wood produced in the forest came from clear felling, the rest from thinnings. Only in the late 1970s, 80s and 90s did felling proceed on a substantial scale. For a long period of time therefore, between c.1940 and 1980, the forest mainly produced thinned poles, rather than mature timber. The story of how this material was processed, and disposed of in an economic way, is an interesting one.

The first thinnings, which took place on a relatively small scale during the 1939-45 War, were made under the auspices of the Timber Production Department. The thinned material was taken to a number of small conversion depots - at Swaffham Heath, Drymere, Didlington, Brandon, and Culford - which had primarily been established to process conifer and hardwood poles taken from the older, private woodlands in the area. After the end of the War in 1945, however, thinning began in earnest. The Commission was fortunate in having a ready-made market for the thinned poles: they were purchased by the National Coal Board for use as pit props in English coal mines. There was a national shortage of material suitable for this purpose due to the intensive wartime exploitation of Britain's reserves of woodland. The coal mines in the Midlands, and in the North East, had long used peeled and seasoned roundwood pit props, many of them imported. The Commission now made a successful bid to capture this lucrative market, in order to ensure that the thinnings from the forest, as well as the final clear fellings, would produce a reasonable profit.

Billy Steel remembered how the sorting and processing of the thinnings was carried out in the forest in the late 1940s:

In the early stages, when they did the thinning, the produce was graded on the rideways or the racks ... All the straightest poles were picked up and numbered, and then the saw bench came along, and cut them into pit props. Now before they did that, the straightest ones had to be peeled by hand, with an ordinary spade - an ordinary garden spade. That's why we had to get on to the men, to make certain that the knots were trimmed up, straight you see, so that the men could peel them. Then they were put on the saw bench, and you had to cut your props like this: whatever your material is, if its a four-foot prop, it must be four inches across the top; and if its a three-foot prop, it must be about three inches across the top ... When they went into the colliery, if they had snags on, etc., the men down the colliery were in their bare skins, and it used to cut their shoulders. You had to make certain that all your props were perfectly clean, with no snags on.

Not all the thinned material was suitable for use as pit props. The thinner poles and

19. Charcoal burning at Brandon Central Depot, c.1960.

the tops of the larger ones had other uses. Some were made into fencing posts; others were sold for use as scaffolding. The smallest ones were converted into pea-poles, for use in gardens, or into netting-stakes for the local rabbit warrens. The curved poles, and irregularly-shaped cuttings, were simply sold as firewood.

In 1946 it was decided to establish a central processing depot on 24 acres (c.10 hectares) of open heath beside the railway station at Brandon (a site already partly in use as one of the small Timber Production Department depots) (Figure 18). The Brandon Central Depot, as this came to be known, was primarily involved in the processing of poles for pit props destined for the East Midlands coalfields. The thinned material was now brought out of the forest by lorry to be stripped and sawn, rather than being processed on the ride sides in the way described above. The wood was also stored here while it seasoned. The Depot had a crane to off-load the lorries, and a number of Liner saw benches, but otherwise consisted of a small collection of buildings, and a vast storage area. Indeed, Brandon was probably the largest timber processing plant ever established in Britain, and made a considerable impact on the local landscape. From here, the cut and seasoned props could be loaded on to railway trucks and taken by train to their destination. By 1950 a hundred men were employed at the depot, but this number was reduced to around 60 during subsequent years, as it was discovered that hand peeling of the poles in the forest was, in fact, more economical. There was thus, in part, a return to the old system of ride-side processing, resulting in a flow of labour out from Depot to forest; although the cutting and, of course, the seasoning of the poles continued to take place at Brandon.

Large amounts of waste material were generated by the processing of thinnings at the Depot, and in time this attracted a secondary industry to the site: charcoal burning (Figure 19). Graham Hobbs later recalled how this enterprise

*Was part of the Brandon Depot but it was private ... The charcoal plant was just down at the end of the Depot, and we used to take all the waste wood down to it. When I first went there we used to be paid a royalty on it. The charcoal was supposed to have gone out over the weighbridge. It was a fellow called * doing it at that time. Of course, a lot of the charcoal went out when the depot was closed: we never did get paid for it. So I thought I'd change all this.*

20. The Novaboard Factory on the outskirts of Thetford, c.1964.

*I said: `right, we'll sell all the firewood down to * by the ton, all the waste wood and that will go over the weighbridge'. Of course, he kicked up about it, but I didn't have to worry about the charcoal then.*

The quantity of thinnings produced by the forest rose rapidly during the 1940s: large areas had, as already noted, been planted around the same time, and thus required thinning at the same time. By 1950, 46,000 tons of thinnings were being extracted each year, more than the Coal Board required, and the Commission were constantly seeking new outlets for this material: for only by selling it could the income be generated to cover the costs of further thinning. By 1950 many of the smaller poles were being cut up and taken to a London factory for conversion to wallboard, while some of the larger material was cut up into short lengths and sent to Bowaters' factory at Sittingbourne in Kent to be turned into wood pulp. By 1959, some 60 tons of pine was being sent each week to a wood wool factory at Manchester. Nevertheless, the problem of finding suitable outlets did not go away, and appears to have become particularly acute around 1960, when vast areas were due (or overdue) for thinning. Successive reports produced by the Commission suggested that lack of boardmill outlets, and a decline in the demand for pit props, were the major restrictions on thinning. By 1962 the work was in serious arrears (a situation exacerbated by government restrictions on the number of workers who could be employed by the Commission, and general recruitment problems). In 1959 a more local market outlet for this kind of material was negotiated. The firm of Novabord Ltd. announced their intention to build a new board-making factory at Thetford, which would utilise much of the Commission's local production of small pine (Figure 20). A contract was signed in 1961, and the supply of chipwood and saw logs began in 1963. In 1964, however - just two weeks after the official opening ceremony - the factory was bought by the British Match Co. Ltd. Deliveries were almost immediately suspended for three months, and when resumed were at less than half the previous rate, and on less favourable terms (although the Commission received £8,000 in compensation). By 1966 the thinning problem was again acute and the Commission's Working Plan report for that year complained that long-term market planning was almost impossible. Indeed, it would appear that the economic disposal of thinnings continued to be a problem into the 1970s: by then, the forest had matured to such an extent that the amount being extracted had declined markedly relative to the amount of timber produced by clear fellings.

Not all the thinned material was taken to Brandon. In the 1950s there were smaller depots at High Lodge and Didlington, for loading sawlogs onto customers' own lorries. In addition, large numbers of the smaller thinnings were taken to the Commission's own Creosote Plant, which had been established in 1958 near the District Offices at Santon Downham. Its purpose was to

Utilise small sized thinnings of Scots and Corsican pines for the production of high quality fencing materials for supply to both their own forests in East England and to the agricultural fencing market.

21. The Creosote Plant, Santon Downham, in the 1960s: the seasoning shed.

Untreated fencing posts have a relatively short life; but those well-seasoned, and properly treated with the correct kind of creosote, can last for fifteen years or more. The plant's buildings and auxiliary works were simple, but effective (Figures 21and 22). They were largely constructed from materials salvaged from redundant military camps in the region. There were four sections in the plant, all connected by a narrow-gauge railway on which manually-operated bogies were mounted. The first was the peeling and pointing shed. From here, the shaped posts were taken to the extensive seasoning sheds, where they were left under cover for lengths of time which varied with the thickness of the pole in question (four weeks, roughly, for each 1" of top diameter). After seasoning the stakes were loaded into welded tubular cradles, likewise placed on bogies, and taken to the creosote tanks. Each cradle held around 150 stakes, 51/2 feet long, and the five tanks could each take two cradles at a time. Fires were lit beneath the tanks and the temperature of the creosote raised to around 170 degrees Fahrenheit. The cradles were lifted into the tanks, and the temperature maintained at this level for two or three hours. The fires were then extinguished and the tanks allowed to cool. The following day, the posts having soaked all night, the fires were relit and the temperature raised again, this time to around 190 degrees. The stakes were then lifted out, drained, placed on the bogies, and taken to the stackyards, where they were stacked in piles pending collection by lorry.

The fires were fed with forest waste - offcuts from the thinnings, peeled bark, and trees killed by disease or insect pests - and this made the plant fairly economical to operate. But an alternative, more efficient, yet more capital-intensive method, `pressure creosoting', was also available locally by the early 1970s, just across the road from the Brandon Depot on the premises of Calders, the private timber company. Calders were one of the main customers for the Commission's increasing output of sawlogs, as the size of the thinned poles increased year by year, and as the first clear fellings began. This may partly explain why the Commission was reluctant to invest in the replacement of the rather antiquated Santon plant with a more modern, Pressure Creosoting facility. The plant was finally closed in 1970, and stake production was concentrated at Brandon.

22. The Creosote Plant, Santon Downham, in the 1960s: the creosoting tanks.

Indeed, in a number of ways the Commission's `dual role' - as raw material producer and supplier on the one hand, and as a wood and timber processor, in competition with many of its principal customers, on the other - became increasingly problematic during the 1960s and 1970s. The issue was one which eventually affected not only the Santon creosote plant but also the Brandon Central Depot itself. In Graham Hobbs' words:

> *Brandon Depot had a sort of question mark hanging over it because they, the `powers that be', whoever they are, said it was competing against the trade, which were our customers for sawlogs and things like that, and it was always a ticklish area. The time I was there, one year we got 54,000 cubic metres through the place. That's a lot of timber.*

But the principal threat to the Central Depot came from a more complex mixture of interrelated changes: in the character of the available technology; in the nature of the markets for forest products; and in the composition of the forest itself. Up until the mid-1960s, the Depot was flourishing. Indeed, from 1963, with the advent of mechanised pole length peeling, stripping of poles was concentrated once again at the site, rather than out in the forest on the ride sides: and cut, processed poles were being supplied to a range of markets. In 1963 and 1964 extensive metalling of the site (long overdue) was carried out. But the expansion of the pulp and chipboard markets made it unnecessary to send so much material through the Depot. Short lengths of thinnings could be loaded without further processing on to customers' lorries, and the widespread adoption of chainsaws in the early 1960s (which made it possible to efficiently convert bent poles to the kinds of short lengths suitable for pulp and chipboard manufacture without removing them to the Central Depot) made the facility even less necessary. To some extent the Commission had always tried to maximise the amount of timber sold standing or unprocessed. This aim could now more easily be realised, and by the end of the decade, only the straight, small-to-medium-sized lengths suitable for pit props, splits, wood-wool billets, posts, stakes and rails were coming to Brandon, for peeling, further conversion, and seasoning prior to dispatch. All the material destined for pulping, and for the boardmills, was marketed direct from the forest.

At the same time two other developments threatened the viability of the Depot. As the forest matured, the size of the thinned material being removed inexorably increased, and clear felling of mature areas began. By 1975 clear felling accounted for almost a third of the total volume of timber coming out of the forest. Much larger material was thus being produced, and this allowed the development of an important sawlog market, with felled timber being sold direct from the forest to the timber merchants. The days of the Central Depot were numbered. By the mid 1970s only a third of the volume of timber being produced from the forest passed through Brandon, and there were plans to close it.

Yet, perhaps surprisingly, the Depot still had several years of useful life left. Indeed, it experienced something of a renaissance. The National Coal Board not only remained an important customer for the kind of medium-sized poles processed here but during the 1970s it embarked on a positive programme of import substitution. By the end of the decade it had abandoned almost entirely the use of imported props. The manager appointed to the Central Depot in 1970, Graham Hobbs, instituted a vigorous programme of modernisation and mechanisation, and there was a significant increase in output. In the early 1980s there was further redevelopment involving the expenditure of some £740,000 on new plant and equipment. But when this programme was only half-completed the miner's strike of 1984 and the subsequent policy of `rationalisation' in the mining industry led to a dramatic decline in the demand for pit props. By this time, moreover, the prices for sawlogs sold direct from the forest became increasingly competitive with that which could be obtained for Depot products. The closure of the plant was announced in November 1987, and was completed by the end of September the following year.

The Changing Workforce

There were many changes in the way that the forest was organised and administered during the 1940s, 50s, and 60s. During the Second World War, the Forestry

Commission was divided into two sections, the Timber Production Department, responsible for the extraction and processing of raw material from the Nation's plantations; and the Forest Management Department, which managed the woods. In the post-War period, the government's `Post-War Forest Policy' document (drawn up in 1943) initiated further changes, including the devolution of some decision-making away from London, and the replacement of the old Divisional Officers by `Conservators'. All this made little difference to the management of the Thetford Forest. At a local level, the most important changes were in the number and configuration of `beats'. These had gradually increased in number during the inter-war years, as the forest steadily expanded, reaching a peak of 18 by the mid-1950s. Their numbers then declined once more, at first gradually, then quite suddenly, in a drastic reorganisation in 1972.

More far-reaching than any of these administrative developments, however, were the various changes in the nature of the forest workforce and in the tools and methods which they employed. As already noted, the War years saw, for the first time in the forest's history, a drastic shortage of labour, as local men joined the forces or took up other jobs. Recruitment became so serious - especially among the supervisory grades - that in 1942 drastic solutions were mooted.

Owing to the constant drain on supervisory staff and the most intelligent of the labourers, a time is envisaged when the quantity of thinning to be done on Thetford Chase cannot all be marked by the supervisory staff.

A rough rule-of-thumb method was instituted so that the semi- and unskilled men could select timber for thinning on their own. More radical still, the same report pointed out that:

The woman measurer appointed on the Chairman's instructions at Rendlesham had proved to be extremely valuable and it was suggested that an intelligent woman could well be trained in the marking of thinnings. The Chairman was completely in accord with the idea and said that the forest would undoubtedly benefit considerably by a number of superior young women who could be trained to carry out technical field work such as thinning.

There was a significant increase in the number of women employed in the forest at this time, especially in the nurseries, but also driving, and carrying out heavy work like brashing, thinning, and processing pit props (Figure 23). Women were employed by the Timber Production Department, and by 1943 the Womens' Land Army had a training camp at Wordwell, towards Bury St Edmunds, on the edge of the forest. Graham Hobbs recalled working with them when he was a young boy of sixteen.

I helped to build a sawmill there for training these girls to use saws and drive tractors and lorries. And then when I finished saw-milling I went into the forest as a tree feller, and I worked quite a lot with them. There was a big gang of timber girls in the Swaffham area, and we were felling a lot of woods around there, and I worked with them. What I was to do was go round with an axe preparing the trees. You had to notch a tree a

23. *Women working a Liner saw bench in Thetford Forest, c.1943.*

certain way to make it fall a certain way and then two of these girls used to come along with a cross-cut saw behind me, things like that. The girls came from all over the country, really: some Scots, a lot from Nottingham. They were pretty good, a lot of them.

With the end of the war, however, women workers gradually disappeared from the forest. Betty Witta recalled how she started work here in 1946:

There were about four of us when I started. They did have more women before then, during the war time ... After that time, when I started, they gradually began to fall off because the men were coming back from the War.

In 1946 the Forest Workers Training Scheme was set up, providing one year's training for demobbed servicemen in actual working conditions. Recruitment was easy once again, especially as a shortage of local housing meant that a job bringing accommodation had a particular appeal. In the new climate of post-War Britain, attitudes and conditions changed. As we have seen, before the War the organisation of the forest workforce had been fairly hierarchical: the foresters were quite distinct from the non-salaried gangers and forest workers. Now, however, casual labour was gradually dispensed with, as the Commission sought to establish a full-time, trained body of forest workers. Moreover, for some tasks piece-rate working was gradually replaced by fixed day wages, or by some combination of the two forms of remuneration, as Betty Witta, who worked in the forest in the 1940s, recalled:

If at the end of the day you'd earnt more than your day pay, then you had your piecework money. It varied really. If you did verge brashing, which'd be the first rows at the side of a compartment, and pull the brash all in, that used to be 5s 9d, I think, or 5s 6d a chain. We used to go in chains. And if you did the ride, complete through brashing, which was a chain wide, and a chain long, that used to be 7s 6d. So you had to work really hard, there's no two ways. It wasn't an easy job. That's why you didn't need any diets!

But thinning, and later felling, was all still usually done on straight piece-rates. There were changes, too, in the character of the District Officers and Conservators. In Arthur Cadman's words

The War came and that changed things. Afterwards we got a rather different type of person who hadn't got the country background but had a longing to work in the country. They were trained in the same way. That class of chap turned out very well, very efficient, but they hadn't got the country background which was a bit of a pity in a way. They didn't understand shooting and they didn't understand all the other country things. They would know all about a bird or animal that had the slightest impact on forestry, they didn't know anything about all the other birds that were in the forest.

There was also a steady growth during the post-War years in the number of people employed in the forest, largely because of the increasing demand for labour as more and more of the plantations came ready for thinning. In 1939, 250 people had been employed by the Commission. By 1950 this figure had more than doubled, to around 570, including around 100 former members of the Polish army. The Commission duly improved its housing provision with the creation, from 1949, of the new `model village' near to the site of the old hall at Santon Downham (Figure 24). By 1951 this settlement housed 287 people. At the same time, forest smallholdings declined steadily in number, continuing a process which had begun in the pre-War years, as forestry work became less seasonal in character, and employment more regular. By the early 1950s few smallholdings seem to have been in existence.

Unfortunately for the Commission this local abundance of labour did not last, and before long it was once again experiencing problems with recruitment. With the development of the `new town' at Thetford from the late 1950s more work was available locally. The housing supplied by the Commission was also now less of an attraction, because of the increasing availability of council houses - which were generally built in better (or at least in more convenient) locations, and which were invariably connected to mains electricity and water - which was not always the case with the Commission's accommodation. Council accommodation also offered greater long-term security, especially as the Commission at this time would not make any firm commitments to house its workers on their retirement.

Problems of recruitment continued into the 1960s and were exacerbated by government restrictions on the amount of money available to pay for labour. It was particularly hard to attract good gangers, and the Commission were acutely aware

24. The forest village, Santon Downham, in the 1950s

that this was due to the poor conditions and remuneration they were able to offer. There was less of a problem in recruiting forest workers. As a report in 1962 pointed out, `pieceworkers on thinning and felling are considerably better off than the great majority of farm workers'. Nevertheless, shortage of labour led to many modifications in established practices in the forest: by the late 1950s, for example, `beating up' was only being carried out within plantations that had a failure rate of more than 20%, and in the following decades it was given even less priority.

Recruitment problems eased through the late 1960s, however, for fewer men were now needed by the Commission. The workforce, numbering some 570 in 1950, had fallen to 350 by 1959, and by 1975 was down to 245. There were a number of reasons for this decline. In part, particularly in the 1960s, it was due to government economies, to restrictions on the number of men the Commission was allowed to employ - restrictions compounded by the financial difficulties resulting from the failure of the Commission to find sufficient commercial outlets for thinnings. Later, there were changes in the nature of the work which needed to be carried out in the forest, with a decline in brashing and thinning relative to felling. But above all the demand for labour fell because of the adoption of mechanised methods of planting and felling: the use of planting machines (beginning in the early 1960s with the Lowther machine); mechanical choppers, bush-cutters, and swipes to clear the ground prior to planting; and, in particular, chainsaws. The latter only became common in the forest as late as 1960 (Figure 25). They increased piece-rate earnings considerably - it was estimated that some men could earn as much as £20 per week,

25. Thinning the forest, c.1965. Chainsaws only came into general use in the forest after 1960.

not a bad wage in the early 1960s - but their widespread use considerably reduced the number of workers required. The need for manpower was also reduced by the use of chemical weed-killers, although manual control of weeds in newly-established plantations went on surprisingly late in the forest. Indeed, even in 1959 the use of chemicals for the control of brambles and rough grasses was only at the experimental stage. Graham Hobbs recalled the early use of chemical weed-killers by the Commission:

So the work that had been done with reap hooks was done with chemicals, very crude chemicals in those days. It was very dangerous really. We messed around with 2-4-5T, we didn't know what we were doing. We were assured by people who should know better that these things were safe. We found out afterwards that they weren't safe.

Safer forms were soon adopted, however, and had a major impact on the management of young plantations.

By the mid-1970s the number of workers employed by the Forestry Commission in Breckland had returned, more or less, to the levels of the 1930s. But the amount of work they did, aided by modern technology, was now much greater, and (even allowing for the cavalier use of weedkillers in the 1960s) the conditions under which they worked had unquestionably improved. Today many retired forest workers would probably contrast the working conditions in the early days of the Commission with those of more recent times, agreeing with Rex Witta's comments:

You know, you hear people say that they're not very good employers, but I've never found that. The only thing that I would say is that they were a bit shortcoming on the wages side in the early days, but everybody was the same ... Although the wages were poor, and the

26. Hauling timber by tractor, c.1970

work was hard, they were good employers. I'm not saying [that was so] when the forest first started to be planted, because I think they were real Tartars then ... When the men were in the nurseries, when it came time for breakfast, the whistle went, and everybody dropped tools, had the meal where they were, and the whistle'd blow and away they'd start again. If they were two or three minutes late in the morning, they got stood off ...

The forest, and especially the remaining areas of the original planting - the now over-mature stands of pine - seems at times to be a natural landscape, and modern felling policies, as we shall see, are designed to enhance this impression. But it is, of course, a landscape as man-made as the arable fields that surround it. It is, above all, a landscape created by hard work, much of it carried out - until quite recently - by hand. Even in 1960 most felling was still done with saws and axes. Indeed, the short history of Thetford Forest serves as a striking reminder of just how recent is our dependence on chemicals and machines. Within living memory, this was still in many ways a hand-made world.

Chapter 5

Protecting the Forest

Chapter 5. Protecting the Forest

Fire

Thetford Forest was not a gradual, organic growth. It was a sudden and essentially unnatural imposition upon the landscape, and this made it vulnerable to a wide range of threats. The most serious of these, from the earliest days, was fire. Conifer plantations are much more combustible than deciduous woods (`native woodland burns like wet asbestos' in the words of the eminent woodland historian, Oliver Rackham). In Breckland this problem was exacerbated by climatic factors - exceptionally low rainfall and humidity - and geological ones - the absence, over wide areas, of any surface water.

Fire was a hazard even when the pines were very young, because the clearance of weed-growth, which usually took place in the early and middle summer, created piles of dry, highly combustible vegetation. The removal of the cut undergrowth from the young plantations would have been impossibly expensive and time-consuming, and so it was simply left in long ridges between the rows of growing trees. The newly-established plantations were thus criss-crossed with lines of highly flammable material. But fire became a much more serious threat as the years passed. The greatest risk came during the `thicket' stage, after five to ten years of growth, when the trees formed a low, bushy, and dense mass (Figure 27). There were a number of fires in the late 1920s, and 1933 was a particularly bad year. Not

27. Plantations at the thicket stage, after five or ten years growth, were particularly susceptiple to fire.

only did the thick growth of vegetation provide a great deal more combustible material. It also made it harder to gain access to burning areas. This was one of the reasons why brashing (the removal of side branches to a height of around six feet (two metres), when the tree was about 20 feet (six metres) high) became standard practise in the forest. But a number of other fire-prevention and fire-control methods were developed as the forest matured, some of which have left an enduring mark upon the landscape.

One practice, adopted from the earliest days of the forest, was to plant belts of less combustible hardwood trees, particularly along roadsides. Today these strips of beech, lime, oak, chestnut and other species form a particularly distinctive and attractive element of the landscape, and it is often assumed that they were originally established mainly for aesthetic reasons, to limit the visual impact of the serried rows of conifers and thus mitigate public criticism of large scale afforestation (Figure 29). There is, however, little indication of such concerns in the documents surviving from the 1920s and 30s and although amenity considerations were of some importance (especially in the later stages of planting) the deciduous strips were mainly established as a fire protection measure. It was assumed that most fires were likely to originate from the roads running through the forest - started by lighted matches or cigarettes dropped by passers-by, or by sparks from steam-powered vehicles, which were still then a common sight. Indeed, a report drawn up in March 1934

28. A major fire somewhere in Thetford Forest, c.1940.

29. Roadside belts of deciduous trees, a prominent feature of the forest landscape, were mainly planted as a fire-protection measure.

emphasised the extent to which the volume of such traffic had increased on the local roads since the war and was continuing to rise. It is interesting that the original purpose of the roadside belts seems to have been largely forgotten in the forest.

In many places, additional protection against fire was provided by leaving unplanted cordons between the perimeter belts and the main body of the plantation. These were generally around 60 feet (20 metres) wide and usually had a central strip, 20 feet (c.6 metres) or more in width, which was either ploughed or burnt under controlled conditions in order to keep it free of vegetation. At a distance further back into the plantation, and parallel to the first cordon, was another wide ride, again about 60 feet wide and with a ploughed strip in the middle. As an article in the Forestry Commission's *Journal* described in 1934:

> *As regards the distance which the second line should be from the first, this depends a good deal on local conditions and topography. On the one hand it should not be so far away that any very great amount of damage will be caused before a fire which has crossed the first line reaches it, but on the other hand it is even more important that it should be sufficiently far back to give time for men to be concentrated on it well before the fire arrives.*

The width of the ploughed strips could also vary, some being rather wider than the common 20 feet. Wider strips were sometimes created around the plantations in the more remote parts of the forest.

> *No economic fire ride can be relied upon as an automatic stop by itself, but the*

wider the ploughing or fire trace the more automatic would it become, and the smaller the

30. The main Peterborough-Norwich rail line between Brandon and Thetford. Steam trains were a major cause of forest fires. The wide, unplanted 'fire traces' either side of the railway line were intended to limit this threat.

number of men by whom it could be defended successfully.

Fire breaks were placed not only on the perimeter of the main forest blocks. After 1933, no area of more than 500 acres (c.200 hectares) was to be without internal subdivision by fire rides so that the extent of damage caused by any fire could be limited. The smaller rides which enclosed and defined the individual compartments were also of some importance in limiting the spread of fire, although their main function, as we have seen, was to provide convenient access to the plantations, for thinning and other activities.

The most serious fire threat came not from cigarettes dropped on roadsides, or sparks from steam-driven road vehicles, but from steam trains. The main railway line from Peterborough to Norwich ran (and still runs) right through the centre of the main area of the Forest. The sparks from trains frequently caused fires in spite of the fact that a strip some 2 chains (c.40 metres) wide was left unplanted on either side of the line (Figure 30). The threat was most severe during the summer, not merely because the vegetation was drier then, but also because the volume of traffic was greater. Billy Steel, who worked in the forest during the 1930s and 40s, later recalled:

Years ago, in the holidays in the middle of the summer, when all the factories closed, they all used to come down to Yarmouth. My biggest worry was on then. Once I had ninety fires from Brandon station up to Thetford station: the worst day I ever had.

The problem was exacerbated by the fact that the trains stopped at Brandon station to take on water, and then had to run at full throttle in order to get up speed. During the summer holiday period large numbers of forest workers would often be employed fighting fires here. Their task was made especially difficult by the fact that, at this time, there were no supplies of water in the immediate locality, so that the only method of fighting the flames was to beat them down. A fire broom was attached to every telegraph pole along the line, and also at regular intervals along the principal public roads.

As the forest matured the problem posed by the dense growth of the thicket stage were replaced by another. As the trees grew higher, it became increasingly difficult to obtain wide views across the terrain, and thus harder to spot fires in their early stages. By 1934 look-out posts were being erected in the upper boughs of the older trees, and it was predicted that the Commission would soon need to construct large towers, equipped with maps and range-finders and connected to the telephone network. A network of roads was gradually established through the forest during the late 1920s and 30s (partly by the inmates of the labour camps), largely to assist in fire control. Thetford Forest, unlike Rendlesham Forest on the other side of East Anglia, did not suffer from fires caused by enemy bombing during the Second World War. But accidental fires continued to be a problem through the 1940s, with one particularly serious outbreak in 1946, when 225 acres (c.90 hectares) were entirely destroyed.

31. One of the towers erected in the forest in the 1940s: High Lodge, 1949.

The chronic lack of surface water in this dry region greatly hampered fire-fighting efforts. Water could only be pumped for short distances from the principal rivers running through the forest - the Lark, Wissey, etc. - or from the ornamental lakes located within the former grounds of the great houses, like those at Didlington. In the immediate post-war years, this problem was partially alleviated by the purchase from the army of 70 elevated metal water-tanks, each containing between three and five thousand gallons of water, which were scattered at strategic positions through the forest. These were partly replaced in the middle 1960s by large concrete tanks, set into the ground.

The decline in the amount of steam-driven road transport during the post-war years did not lead to any decrease in the risk of fires because, as a report in the 1950s pointed out, a number of new threats had appeared, including an increase in the practise of stubble burning on neighbouring arable land, and a steady growth in the numbers of people coming to visit the forest at weekends. During the 1940s and 50s fire control measures thus continued to develop. Tall look-out towers were erected: six in Thetford Forest - at Swaffham, High Ash, Gallows Hill, Roudham, and High Lodge -and one in King's (Figure 31). Each was connected to the GPO telephone network and was equipped with a log book, clock, binoculars, 1":1 mile Ordnance Survey maps, seat, compass, venetian blinds, and oil stove. They had windows which were marked in degrees, to make it easier to pin-point the direction of a blaze. Sirens were set up at Santon Downham, and a radio station which could communicate with three radio sets carried in landrovers and a further four kept in packs, for use in other vehicles. It was now possible to muster fifty or more men anywhere in the forest in less than forty-five minutes. The railway line was regularly patrolled at high-risk periods, but this practise was ended in 1963, when steam trains were effectively replaced by diesels on the Peterborough-Norwich line.

On the whole, the fire protection measures adopted by the Commission were successful, especially given the excessively dry nature of the local terrain. Although a multitude of small fires broke out within the forest, these seldom developed into anything more serious. Today forest fires are a negligible threat, due in part to the changing (and increasingly varied) age structure of the forest, in part to improved vehicular access and better fire-fighting technology.

Animal Pests

Fire was perhaps the most dramatic threat to the forest, but there were others. Large-scale afforestation radically changed the environment of Breckland and introduced new pests into the area. Deer had been almost unknown in the district before the 1920s but their numbers increased steadily as afforestation proceeded. Roe deer had probably been introduced into the area in the 1880s, by Colonel MacKenzie of Downham Hall, who released several pairs - reportedly brought from Wurtemburg in Germany - in Queen's Wood. Others may also have existed, especially in Lord Iveagh's woods at Elveden, but their numbers remained small until planting began. They had become a serious threat to young trees by the mid 1930s, especially to hardwoods and above all to beech trees, which were repeatedly browsed off to a height of a few inches above ground level. The problem was particularly acute in the Elveden and High Lodge areas, where by 1937 there were reported to be at least 40 roe at large. In 1937 experimental deer-proof fencing was erected around compartments 203, 204, and 207, and was found to be extremely successful in limiting damage. A more widespread policy of fencing was considered, but rejected, because of the vast expense which it would have involved. Only a few experimental plots were ever protected in this way. In 1938, the use of hounds for tracking deer was considered, although rejected because of the potential conflict with sporting interests. A plan was discussed for putting a man armed with a gun into every beat `With a roving commission, his competence being judged by the head of deer he brought in'.

These precise proposals were rejected, but a policy of intensive shooting and trapping was adopted throughout the 1930s. This slackened during the war, however, and during the post-War years the numbers of roe deer continued to increase. By the 1950s red deer had also become established, especially in the eastern sections of the forest. Their origin is uncertain, but they may have escaped while being hunted as `carted deer' in the 1920s (hunting carted deer involved bringing an animal to a spot in the open countryside, releasing it, chasing and recapturing it, and then bringing it home again). Whatever their origins the local environment was well suited to them, because the browse available within the forest itself could be supplemented in the winter months by the various crops growing in the neighbouring arable fields, especially roots like turnips and swedes. Fallow deer, probably descended from escapees from Livermere Park, were also well-established in King's Forest by 1940. By 1953 muntjac had begun to appear. By this time much of the forest was reaching maturity, and the main problem was no longer the deers' predilection for the young foliage but rather their tendency to strip bark. The Commission needed to take decisive action, but the old, somewhat indiscriminate forms of control were no longer acceptable, given that this was a time when members of the general public were visiting the forest in ever-increasing numbers. Rex Witta recalled how it was then that

The Commission first had the idea to set up a wildlife side, or a ranger side, because in one of the areas a couple of old ladies were out walking and they found a deer in a snare, and of course they went to the papers. And that set them thinking, that the public were on their backs.

In 1956 selective culling by rifle was introduced, and in 1960 deer wardens, paid as warreners, were appointed for each district. One of the first was Rex Witta: his brief was `to keep the numbers of deer down to a very low level, plus shoot or catch as many rabbits or hares as I possibly could'.

Deer numbers were subject to a number of other checks, beyond the direct control of the Forestry Commission. The numbers of red deer were, to some extent, kept down in the 1960s and 70s by the activities of poachers. Rex Witta recalled how:

Red deer went down pretty drastically when the price of venison went up, in the seventies I think that was ... The other thing that played a big part in the depopulation was the fact that our felling programmes increased, taking the old habitat away ... And in a way, although I was saddened to see the numbers go down, I was also pleased by the fact that the big herds that we used to have here (I mean, it was nothing to see 40 or 50 red deers in a group) disappeared. The herd split up into much smaller groups.

Today the Commission's rangers continue to cull deer on a systematic basis, seeking not to eradicate them but rather to maintain numbers at sustainable levels, which would conflict neither with the needs of forestry nor with the agricultural operations of the Commission's neighbours.

Deer were, to a large extent, a problem of the Commission's own making: few had existed in Breckland before the forest was planted. Rabbits in contrast were a long-established pest which continued to be a problem long after the initial planting. Wherever the fencing around young plantations was damaged - as occurred in many parts of King's Forest during the 1940s, as a result of tank manoeuvres - the rabbits got in and damage occurred. Nearly 50% of the plantations in King's were destroyed between 1947 and 1951 as a result of rabbit attack. In March 1947 alone 80,000 rabbits were taken in 6,000 acres (c.2,400 hectares) of unbrashed plantation by five, later twelve, warreners using nets, snares, traps, and guns. Afterwards, the rabbit burrows were destroyed, and the most severely damaged areas were completely replanted. As late as 1950 the Commission was employing 30 warreners on a regular basis. At various times in the 1920s and 1930s the Commission contemplated more widespread and systematic schemes of rabbit extermination, but these never came to anything. This was largely because of the opposition of the local sportsmen, whether neighbouring landowners or the Commission's own sporting tenants. The rabbit problem was greatly alleviated by the onset of myxomatosis in 1952/3 but numbers recovered surprisingly quickly and by 1964 it was reported that, in some parts of the Forest, populations had returned to pre-disease levels. Until relatively recently, the Commission supported one of the few Rabbits Clearance Societies still functioning in Britain. As Rex Witta pointed out in 1990:

Without the help that that warrener and his lads have given us over the past five or six years I think we'd have been in serious trouble in some parts. The chap who does the warrening, he's an expert. His father was doing it. You see, we lost all our expertise when all the warreners went. Long net, ferrets, all sorts of things ...

The problem was now, however, more localised, for two reasons. Although rabbit numbers did recover quite quickly from myxomatosis they never returned to earlier levels, and recurrent epidemics continue to decimate populations. More importantly, the changing environment of the Forest made the area less suitable for the animals. Rabbits thrive best in open country, in areas of grass and heath. They are less suited to mature woodland. As larger and larger areas were planted up and as the pines grew tall and shaded out much other vegetation, rabbit numbers inevitably declined. Today rabbits remain a problem but mainly where the plantations are less extensive and continuous, intermixed with or adjoining areas of arable land, or pockets of heath.

Hares can also be a problem, especially when areas have just been planted. As Rex Witta again explained:

The annoying thing about it is, when we planted up a new site, a new compartment, if you don't keep a careful watch on it, then a fortnight, three weeks, we've had up to 85% of the trees damaged. They go along the rows and just nip the tops out. The rabbits will eat what they damage: but the hares just nip along, and nip the tops out, and leave them lying there. What happens then, when the next year's growth comes, the tree out what we call stag-headed - multi-headed - and they don't get a nice straight stem then.

Other animals have taken their toll, especially squirrels. Even voles are said to have caused serious damage on one occasion (in 1941), when they stripped the bark from a low-lying Douglas fir plantation. Hardly surprising, then, that until the 1960s the Commission's attitude to animal life within the forest was one of considerable, if not unremitting, hostility. It is true that much interest was shown in the bird life, and how this changed as the forest matured. But, according to Rex Witta, up until the 1960s `... all the rabbits, hares, deer - anything that looked at a tree - the forester thought was going to damage it'.

But it was insects rather than mammals that posed the more serious threat to the growing plantations. In particular, the Pine Shoot Moth (*Evetria buoliana*) caused extensive damage to Scots pines in the 1920s and 30s. The attack of the moth caused severe deviation from the vertical axis, producing trees with deformed growth. There were fears that vast areas of the forest might be ruined but these proved unfounded. The damage eased, probably due to the establishment of a natural biological check, although as late as 1959 severe attacks were still being experienced by young Scots pine plantations, especially in the Mildenhall area. Few signs of the damage caused are now evident in the forest landscape, for nearly all the damaged trees have been removed during thinning. Other insect pests rose to prominence as the years passed and the character of the forest changed: especially as thinning and, in particular, clear felling began. The Pine Shoot Beetle (*Tomicus piniperda*) effected forest management practices because its control required that all rough-barked pine must be removed from forests and depots, or else peeled or sprayed, within six weeks of felling between early March and mid-July. The Black Pine Beetle (*Hylastes ates*) and the Pine Weevil (*Hylobius abietis*) are similarly associated with clear felled areas: young replacement trees in badly effected compartments have to be sprayed with insecticide.

The Fungal Threat

The greatest threat to develop as the forest matured was not animal but fungal: *Fomes annosus* or, as it is now known, *Heterobasidion annosum*. *Fomes* first became a problem when thinning began. The airborne spores of the fungus took hold in the stumps of felled trees, then spread through the root system to infect the roots of adjacent, standing trees, damaging and eventually killing them. Spreading from tree to tree, the fungus soon produced ever-widening circles of dead and dying timber.

The problem was first noted during `pre-thinning' in the late 1930s, but the deaths were originally attributed primarily to waterlogging or drought: the fungus itself was regarded as a secondary manifestation of stress. Before long, however, the true extent of the problem became apparent, although there was some initial confusion about the precise mechanisms involved in the development and spread of the fungus, and its appearance seems to have caused alarm and confusion. In a letter written in February 1946 W.H. Guillebaund, the Commission's Director of Research, described how he found a recent report on *Fomes* `extremely interesting but rather startling'.

It is indeed an extraordinary thing that the attack by Fomes should have followed so quickly after thinning. I would have been prepared to forecast some kind of trouble in those plots which were heavily thinned but I never would have thought that the pre-thinning would have led to the same consequences.

In 1946 the Commission's annual report described how:

Die-back resulting from the attack by the root fungus Fomes annosus in 20 to 25 year old plantations of Scots and Corsican pines in East Anglia has caused appreciable losses in certain compartments. The causes of the outbreak are under investigation.

The following year a report described how a large-scale survey had been carried out and numerous factors investigated.

The work as a whole is still incomplete but it appears that infection is mainly through root contact, and that the stumps of trees removed in early clearings constitute a serious source of infection, and further that the disease tends to be worse on alkaline soils. The disease, however, is not as widespread as had at one time been supposed.

By 1949 the situation was still worrying enough for the possibility of doing away with thinning altogether to be seriously considered. But later in that year a report stated that 'The initial onset was rapid, and extended over a number of Compartments in different blocks of the forest, but the disease had made little progress, and few new centres of infection have been discovered'.

More was now known about the fungus and treatment methods improved. Initially, there were attempts to control its spread by digging trenches around the infected stumps, as Billy Steel recalled:

We used to dig around those, just take a big trench round these `fairly rings' at odd times. We didn't do a lot of it. Just to see whether we could stop this thing from spreading. And then of course they found it wouldn't stop it. So they introduced, after a man had cut a tree down, he had to treat it with creosote.

This method was universally applied by 1952, but by 1963 a more sophisticated technique had been adopted. The stumps were inoculated with the culture of another fungus, *Peniophera gigantea*. This excluded the *Fomes* spores, and while it fed off the host stump it did not pass through the root system to infect adjacent trees. Billy Steel later recalled the first use of the new method.

They had some factory make it into aspirin tablets like, and the men ... when they finished doing their work, had to go and get the Peniophera out of a bottle and pour this in a tin, with a brush. And we found out, because its white, they didn't know which one had been done or not, so we had to invent a dye - a blue dye.

Today the spores are acquired in small sachets, produced commercially, which are diluted with water. The solution can either be applied to the stumps using special containers after the tree has been felled with a chainsaw, or through a device fixed to the cutting bar of a harvesting machine. Nevertheless, the threat posed by *Fomes* has not gone away. By the time systematic stump treatment had been adopted in the 1950s the fungus had become widely established in the forest, especially on the more calcareous soils, and it can remain active in infected stumps for twenty years or more. When replanting of clear-felled areas first began in the 1960s, as many as 70% of the young trees died in some locations within ten years. As a result, since the early 70s areas to be restocked on the more alkaline soils have been systematically `de-stumped'. Using a hydraulic excavator the stumps are dug out and then pushed into long rows, thus preventing the fungus spreading to the roots of the young trees. Other fungal pests have taken their toll of the forest pines, most notably Peridermium stem rust (*Periderminium pini*), first recognised in the Elveden Beat in the 1940s. But none have had quite the impact upon the forest and its management as *Fomes*.

The forest's susceptibility to fire, and to the depredations of pests like *Fomes*, were largely a consequence of its essentially unnatural, monocultural character, coupled with the fact that it was initially planted in a very short space of time. Large areas thus passed through the same stages of growth at the same time, thus producing great expanses of combustible material at the brushwood stage. Extensive areas were likewise due for felling at the same time, and this - combined with the dominance of a single species - rendered the forest so vulnerable to fungal attack. Yet human ingenuity has triumphed, time and again, over these threats: and the forest has survived.

Chapter 6

New Roles for the Forest

Chapter 6. New Roles for the Forest

There have been many important changes in the appearance of the forest over the last few decades, the consequence both of its arrival at maturity, and of new ideas about how it should be used and managed. The forest was planted with a single purpose - that of providing a succession of homegrown timber which could, in particular, be available at times of national emergency. But during the post-War years it gradually gained a more complex, multi-faceted role: and over the last decade this tendency has been taken further than ever, with far-reaching effects upon the landscape.

Cultivating the Public

We can trace the origins of these changes back into the 1960s. The thinning problem was only one of the difficulties which faced the Commission in the post-War years. It always lacked the continuing government support necessary for the long-term business of forestry, and in the 1950s and 60s the policies of successive administrations seemed at times calculated to alienate the goodwill of its staff. The Commission were forced to sell no less than nine square miles of land between 1951 and 1959, largely for extensions to the War Department's Battle Training Area. Poor morale led to much internal friction, especially between the District Offices at Santon Downham and the main Divisional Offices at Cambridge. In 1962 one report commented 'It often seems that the main work of the Estate Branch consists of negotiating disposal of parts of the estate, and in explaining that funds or staff were not available for repairs or new buildings'.

The last was a reference to the reluctance of the Commission to do anything about the dreadful state of the Santon Downham offices, described in depressing terms in a report of 1963. The buildings, a collection of former War Department huts erected on the site in 1947, were in a terrible condition, with condensation so serious that furniture had to be shifted around to keep it dry. There were leaks in the roof, floods after heavy rain, and the central heating boiler produced bad fumes. 'Its squalid appearance comes as a shock to visitors who approach it through part of the surrounding 53 million hoppus feet of softwood, being grown mainly for building timber'.

The buildings were finally demolished, and the present offices erected, in 1965. But more serious worries remained. Rumours abounded that much of the Mundford Beat was to be taken over by the War Department, for the construction of a gigantic `atom smasher'. One report suggested that `the forest is vulnerable to being whittled away for town expansion, army training, or to any body or department with greater influence than the Forestry Commission'.

This feeling of isolation coincided, however, with a gradual increase in the amount of public recreation taking place within the forest. In the early days this had been at a very low level. As Rex Witta recalled:

It wasn't a thing that ever cropped up. The foot paths were public but there was no Rambler's Association or anybody making a hoo-ha. Very few people used the footpaths: it didn't arise.

But visitor numbers began to increase in the 1950s and 60s. This was partly the result of changing patterns of recreation, partly due to the spread of car ownership, and partly a result of the growth of the nearby town of Thetford. There was also increasing interest in the forest on the part of naturalists. The growth of the pines to maturity, and the creation of open areas by clear felling, was attracting a wider variety of birds, including crossbills: by 1965 sparrowhawks were nesting here. And in a more general way, the changing appearance of the maturing forest made it a more pleasant place to walk or picnic.

All this was initially regarded by the Forestry Commission with mixed feelings. As early as 1959 it was reported that an area by the river at Two Mile Bottom `appears to have become a public camp. People are bathing in the river, there is a wooden hut on wheels, and many fires are being lit' - the last, of course, a serious hazard in this dry and combustible environment. In 1960, barriers were being erected for the first time across the entrances to the main forest rides, in an attempt to keep cars out. But in spite of some difficulties the Commission's staff became more and more interested in cultivating public interest, and in encouraging access and diversifying the forest's use. In 1964 the possibility of making the whole area a `Forest Park' was mooted for the first time, and although the suggestion was rejected there were significant changes in policy. In 1966 for example it was decided that Compartment 101 would henceforth be managed in such a way that `timber production is subordinate to amenity'. Public use of the forest increased steadily through the 1970s: it could now be more easily tolerated because, with much of the forest now grown beyond the thicket stage, there was less risk of serious fires.

It is arguable that, to some extent, the Commission's changing attitude was a response to the lack of consistent support from the government, and in particular in the 1980s to the threat of privatisation - a policy widely considered a `privatisation too far', vigorously opposed by the general public and amenity groups, and eventually withdrawn even by the doctrinaire Conservative government of the day. Either way, by 1985 the Thetford Forest Management Plan was recommending a wide range of measures which would enhance the wildlife importance and visual appearance of the forest. Thus the lines of stumps uprooted as a precaution against *Fomes* were considered `visually intrusive', and it was suggested that they should be screened in some way, or else laid out at an oblique angle to the adjacent roads. The pattern of felling should likewise take account of visual amenity `The scale of fellings ... should be bold, but generally not exceed 10-20 hectares within 300 metres of public roads, or 40 hectares elsewhere.' Things were changing fast.

The Forest Park

All this culminated in May 1990, with the official designation of Thetford as a `Forest Park'. Although this new title did not mark any great moment of change in the life of the forest, it did serve to confirm those alterations of purpose which had been developing steadily over the previous decades. It was now explicitly recognised that while timber production still held a very important place in the management of the forest, its needs had to be balanced with recreational and environmental considerations, and with the overall appearance of the landscape.

This pronounced change in emphasis was made possible by the fact that the forest had reached maturity: the onset of clear felling and restocking provided an opportunity for

32. Clear felling only got underway on a large scale in the 1970s. This photograph shows one of the early areas of clear felling.

a change of course. But change was necessary because of wider political considerations. The idea that publicly-owned land should cater for the needs of local people, and should be available for the use of the population in general, had gradually gained ground. More importantly, the expansion of the government's role in conservation, and its responsibility - recognised in a variety of international treaties - for the quality of the environment as a whole, led to pressure for a good example to be set on state-owned land. A twenty-five year management plan now exists, which explicitly affirms a commitment to the aims of `multi-purpose forestry', in which the requirements of timber production, recreation and conservation are carefully balanced. This plan is to be up-dated every five years in the light of changes occurring both within the forest, and in the wider world.

In 1993 the Forestry Commission was divided into two sections - the Forestry Authority and Forest Enterprise. It is the latter organisation which is responsible for the actual management of the nation's forests. At the top of the tree (so to speak) locally is the Forest District Manager, responsible not only for Thetford but also for the other East Anglian forests. Next in line are three District Foresters: but whereas in the past the forest was divided - for administrative purposes - into specific areas of land, all three of these individuals now takes responsibility for the entire forest, each dealing with a particular aspect of management. One is responsible for the establishment and maintenance of the plantations, one for the harvesting and marketing of the forest products, and one for matters relating to recreation and conservation. The rest of the workforce consists of foresters; rangers (responsible for controlling animal populations in the forest); and forest workers (still the majority of employees); together with a new corpus of recreational staff. In all, around a hundred people are now employed in the forest.

Timber Production

Timber production still has a central role in the multi-purpose forest. The vast majority of the forest's trees reached their optimum age as a timber crop in the 1970s: continuing their existence beyond maturity is uneconomic, since growth slows in later life. Over the past two decades clear felling has therefore become the most important aspect of the forest routine, and some 2,500 trees are extracted from the forest every day - a phenomenal number - producing in all some 180,000 cubic metres of timber per annum (Figure 34). However, as the forest was originally planted with considerable speed -at a greater rate than it is now possible to fell and replant it - some trees are being left to stand longer than would be the case if simple rules of economic forestry were followed. The period of clear felling is being extended, from fifteen to thirty or even forty years. As a result the forest will, in time, gain a more even age-structure, and in the future the work of felling, marketing and replanting

33. A 'Forwarder' at work in the forest in the early 1980s.

will be more evenly spread over time. Current practice thus represents what appears, to the present management, to be the best compromise possible between the creation of a `sustainable forest' and maximising the value of the existing timber.

As we have seen, by the mid-1960s chainsaws had replaced hand felling and tractors were being used to extract timber. The accelerating scale of felling, however, demanded more sophisticated technology and in the early 1980s specially adapted tractors and trailers - known as `Forwarders' - came into widespread operation (Figure 33). Their adoption represented a change not just in technology but also in operating systems. Formerly timber or lengths of log had been dragged to the roadside to be converted into manageable lengths for sale to customers. With the advent of Forwarders, the trees were now converted at the felling site, and loaded by means of an attached hoist into the trailer. But it was in 1991 that mechanisation really reached the forest, with the arrival of the first 'Harvester'. Like the combine harvesters of arable agriculture, these machines perform the entire process of conversion - from standing crop to finished product. The tree is grabbed, cut off at the base, stripped of its branches and cut into logs of the required length in a single, rapid operation of robotic complexity. The remaining debris is sold to contractors, by area, and turned into chipwood on site by machines rather like `forwarders'. Anything remaining is raked into `windrows', together with the stumps, in areas likely to be infested with *Fomes*. Except where other uses of the forest dictate, clear-felled areas are rapidly replanted with Corsican pine, now considered the best timber crop for the poor Breckland soils. Planting, too, has long been mechanised, using a planting machine mounted on the back of a normal agricultural tractor.

One operation is, however, still carried out by hand. 'Beating up', the replacement of trees lost in the early years of growth, still goes on much as before. Not so thinning: in 1992 a second Harvester was purchased by the Commission to carry out this operation, and in the following year a third - designed to deal with late thinning and early clear felling - was added to the forest's stock of equipment.

With the onset of large-scale clear felling in the 1970s the amount of mature timber being produced from the forest increased dramatically, and the methods of marketing the forest's products continued to develop. Today, the bulk of the harvested material consists of sawlogs produced at the felling site. These are sold on to local saw mills. Some of this material still ends up as pit props, but only a small minority: most goes to the building trade, or is used to make fencing posts and pallets. The small round wood is sent to make reconstituted wood board: since the closure of the Novaboard factory in 1972 this material has had to be sent far afield, much of it now going to factories in North Wales. The high transport costs, which are taken into account by the purchasers, considerably reduce the value of what is anyway the least valuable part of the crop.

Recreation in the Forest

Although timber production remains of vital importance it no longer holds quite the overriding position it once did. The amenity aspect has grown steadily and today the forest's recreational potential is a major justification for its existence. It has been estimated that over a million visits are made to the forest each year, and most of the area of the forest park is now freely accessible to the public. While felling and other forestry operations cause the temporary closure of limited areas, sporting rights - once of considerable importance - apply to much less of the forest than formerly, and generally cause only temporary restrictions on access.

A policy of actively encouraging people to come into the forest has led to a steady increase in the number of car-parks, picnic areas and waymarked trails for walkers, cyclists and horse riders. These facilities have been designed not only to provide services for visitors but also to enable recreation in the forest to be controlled and managed, and thus to allow a range of activities, including those associated with timber production, to take place simultaneously without interfering with each other. The number of special events taking place has also increased, and now includes car rallies and mountain bike championships - even husky dog racing. All these likewise need to be carefully managed, in order to maintain the peace and quiet which draws the majority of visitors to the forest.

The growing importance of recreation is most clearly reflected in the opening, in 1992, of the Forest Centre at High Lodge (Figure 34). This was not intended to provide alternatives to existing modes of recreation - walking, picknicking, or bird-watching. Rather, it was established in order to bring in additional groups of people, attracted here by the more ordered nature of the facilities on offer: information, refreshments, souvenirs, and a variety of more structured outdoor activities. There is a children's adventure playground, a `squirrel maze', and a surfaced trail for the disabled (Figure 35). A `tree trail' and a simple orienteering course are also provided, for those who want to learn more about the wider

34. The Forest Centre, High Lodge, was opened in 1992.

recreational opportunities on offer in the forest. More formal educational services are also provided by the Commission, through liaison with local schools: the small class room at the Santon Downham offices has now been replaced by a better-equipped facility at the Forest Centre.

Part and parcel of the Forest's new role has been an increasing willingness to consult the public, and various conservation and amenity organisations, over the ways that the forest should be used and managed. The Friends of the Forest Park was founded in 1996, and recent changes in the design of the forest have, as we shall see, largely been formulated following extensive consultations with visitors.

Landscapes of Conservation and Design

Many visitors come to the forest to look at the wildlife, and it is partly because of this, although also as a response to more general public pressure to give the environment a higher priority, that the role of conservation in the management of the forest has greatly increased over the last decade or so. By the 1990s annual meetings were already being held with interested groups of naturalists and conservationists, where their particular needs could be considered and discussed. In 1991 these arrangements were formalised with the creation of the Conservation Panel, made up of experts in the various relevant fields. In

35. 'Multi-purpose forestry' : children at play on the adventure playground, High Lodge Forest Centre, in 1997.

1992, the year of the Rio Earth Summit, the British government's commitment to increasing care of the environment was reflected in the change of this body's title to the Thetford Forest District Environmental Panel.

English Nature has designated eleven Sites of Special Scientific Interest within the forest. These are, on the whole, fairly small areas, chosen as representative of the principal Breckland habitats. The wetlands which punctuate this largely arid region are well represented: not only valley-floor fens and wet grassland but also those rare and characteristic Breckland features, the fluctuating meres and `pingos' - that is, ponds formed by the freezing and thawing of ice in periglacial conditions during the last Ice Age. These sites survived the early days of the forest because they were unsuitable for planting but have remained vulnerable to other threats - drainage, pollution, etc. Each is now protected by a conservation plan, agreed with English Nature. In addition to these SSSIs, a large number of sites of `wildlife conservation value', many chosen because they are the habitats of particular threatened species, have been identified and given their place in forest planning. But in addition to these outside designations, the Commission itself established its own extensive nature reserve in 1985, when most of the valley of the Little Ouse between Thetford and Brandon - containing areas of alder carr, and stands of poplars, as well as damp grazing meadows, fen and reedbed - was set aside as the Santon and Little Ouse Valley Forest Nature Reserve. In 1987, as part of the Commission's contribution to the European Year of the Environment, a Bird Trail was established, starting within the reserve and marked on the ground by numbered posts and interpreted for the visitor in a leaflet which, together with other publications, is sold at the High Lodge Forest Centre, and at the main Forest Enterprise offices at Santon Downham. Things have moved a long way since 1966, when a policy document roundly declared: `The Forestry Commission will not refrain from acquiring land on the grounds that this would be detrimental to the natural history of the region'.

A range of heathland species - survivors from the old landscape - had clung on in the forest rides, and seventy miles of these have now been made into conservation areas, in which a variety of mowing regimes has been adopted in order to provide a wider range of habitats. The heathland survivors have been able to expand into clear felled-areas, now that harvesting has begun in earnest. The importance of a continuous succession of such sites in close proximity to one another is now recognised by Forest Enterprise, and is taken into account when the felling programme is decided: another interesting example of the ways in which practical matters of forestry are now carefully integrated with the needs of nature conservation. The ecological importance of heathland is being recognised in other ways. One project currently in the planning stage involves the restoration of 300 hectares of heath at the expense of forest. A probable site, beside existing heathland at Weeting Heath, has already been earmarked.

Although the forest contains rare species of many kinds - flora such as the military orchid, rare lichens, butterflies, moths and beetles, birds such as the woodlark and the nightjar, amphibians and reptiles - it is probably the mammals which rank highest in the minds of the general public. In 1990 it was the threatened red squirrel which was adopted as the symbol of the new forest park. This animal, once common throughout Britain, is now rare in England, forced out by competition from the grey squirrel, an immigrant from north America. Thetford Forest is one of its last strongholds. The species can compete much more successfully in tracts of continuous conifer forest, from which the greys cannot easily retreat

36. Landscape by design: 'organic coupes' and over-mature timber near High Lodge in 1997.

to areas of broadleaved trees (their preferred habitat) when supplies of pine cones run low. To encourage its conservation, 1,800 hectares of the forest have been set aside specifically as a red squirrel reserve. The grey squirrels were removed from the area and supplementary feeding provided for the reintroduced reds, which have become the focus for an intensive study. The project is a joint endeavour, involving the Forestry Commission, English Nature, and the People's Trust for Endangered Species.

The other mammals widely associated with the Forest, the various species of deer, do not require the special care afforded the red squirrel. As already noted, these animals find all the protection they need in the ordinary operations of the forest, and still have to be culled to maintain their numbers at a healthy level.

Both for the red squirrel, and for the deer, it is the forest itself which supplies the necessary habitat, not the vestiges of and survivals from the older Breckland landscape. It is important to emphasise that the forest is now of value in its own right, not just as a matrix within which pockets of a displaced heathland flora and fauna live on. And it is mature forest which provides a particularly important habitat, one which would be lost over the next three or four decades if timber production was the only, or the overriding, concern of the forest's administrators. Instead of felling all the original planting from the 1920s and 30s as soon as economically viable, a significant proportion is being retained and allowed to grow on past economic maturity, both for visual amenity and for conservation reasons. The

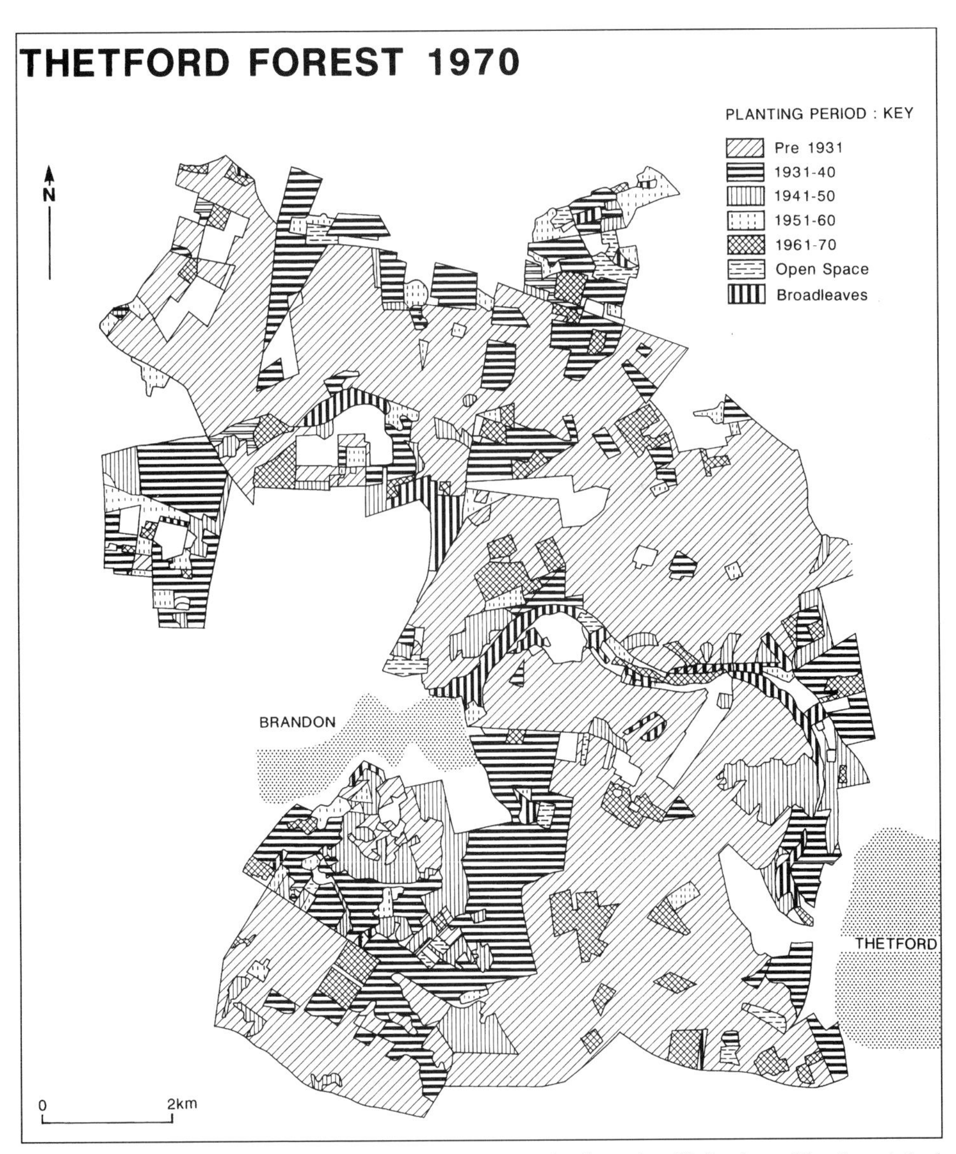

37. (a) The central section of Thetford Forest in 1970. The forest is still dominated by the original planting of the 1920s and 30s, and by a highly rectilinear pattern of rides and compartment boundaries.

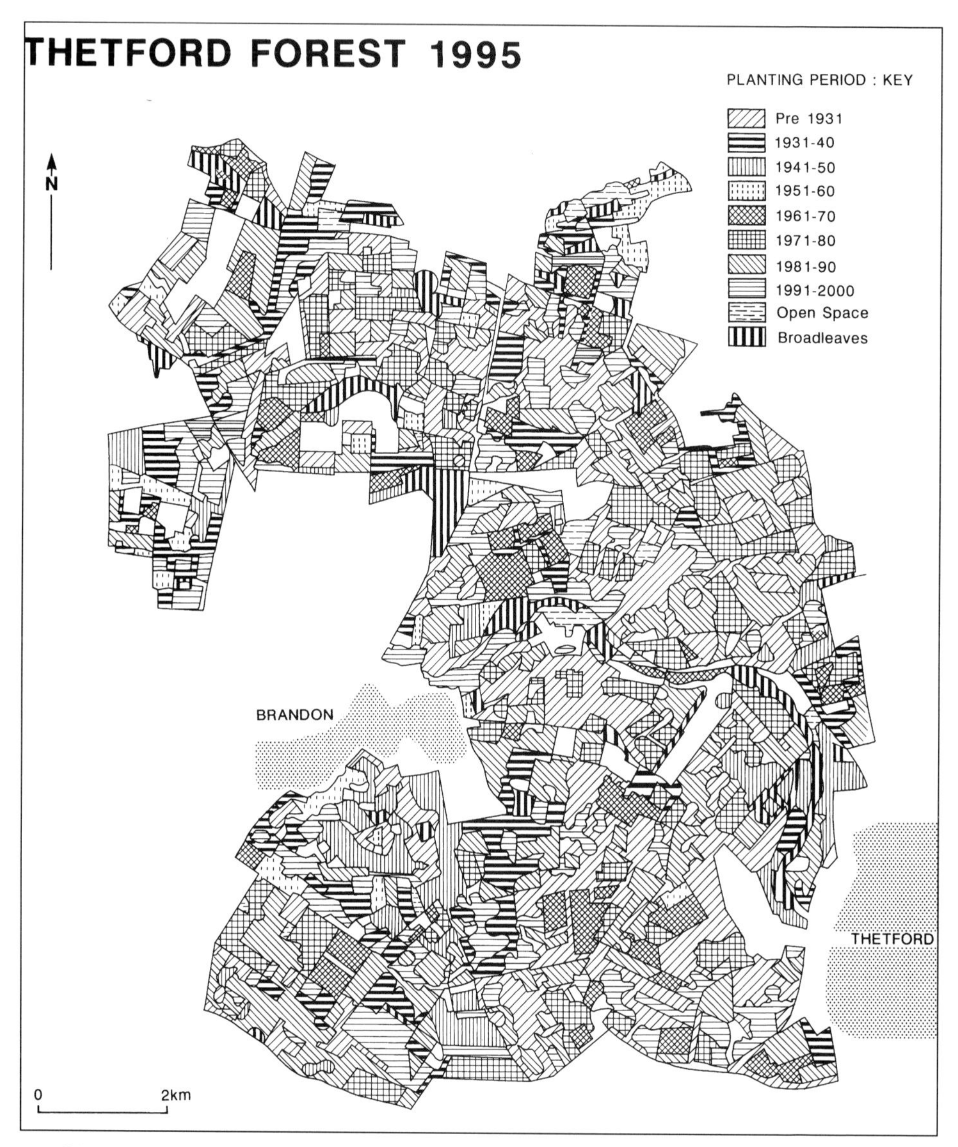

37. (b) By 1995 most of the original trees have been felled, a more even age structure has begun to be established, and a curvilinear pattern of 'organic coups' has started to appear.

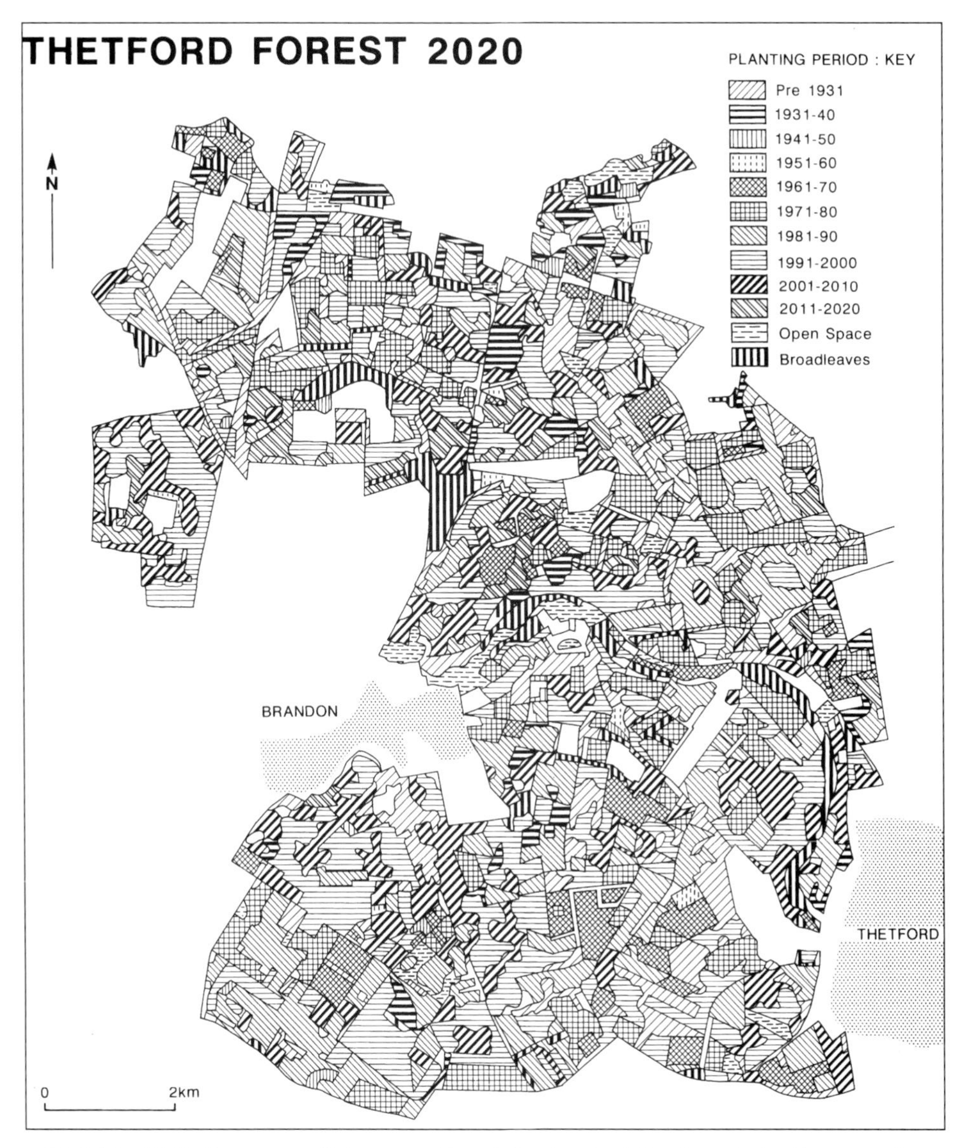

37. (c) By 2010, if current policies are continued, the forest will be characterised by serpentine, curvilinear lines dividing blocks of trees with a wide variety of ages.

intention is to maintain around 1,000 hectares of pre-War conifer plantations into old age. Similar aims now govern policy towards broadleaved trees which, as we have seen, were always difficult to establish, and never accounted for more than 12% of the forest's area. It has been decided to retain this proportion - mostly by natural regeneration in the areas already so occupied. Efforts have also been made to increase the quantity and diversity of the deciduous understorey. In all these ways, the needs of nature conservation have had, and are having, a major impact upon the appearance of the landscape.

Other recent changes to the visual environment of the forest - more far-reaching ones - have occurred for rather different reasons. The appearance of the forest was, until recently, largely a consequence of economic considerations, of matters of practical forestry. This began to change in the 1980s, however, and Thetford forest - like others in Britain - has been subjected to the attentions of landscape architects. It is now being *designed*, in order to present an attractive appearance, following detailed consultations with the general public. Whereas in the past the map of the forest was a patchwork of stern rectangular blocks, the last two decades has seen a carefully planned change to a much softer jigsaw of interlocking curves - so-called `organic coupes' (Figure 36). Priority has been given to the improvement

38. Mature timber being left to grow into old age for reasons of amenity and conservation.

of the view from the main public roads, although the original plans were disrupted somewhat by the great gale of 1987, which did considerable local damage in the forest and so necessitated a number of changes in the felling programme.

The extent and rapidity of the various changes in the appearance and composition of the forest which have taken place over the last few decades - changes caused not only by its arrival at maturity and the onset of large-scale felling and restocking, but also by the various new roles it has adopted - are made clear in Figure 37. In 1970 (Figure 37(a))the forest was still dominated by trees planted in the 1920s and 30s. Felling and restocking had hardly begun. Within less than two decades the bulk of this timber has been removed, and replanting has taken place on a massive scale - although in a phased way, so that the forest can attain a more even age structure. Those trees surviving from the original planting of the 1920s and 30s now make up around 12% of the forest but, as Figures 37(b) and (c) indicate, this percentage will change little over the following decades. These older trees, retained for reasons of amenity and conservation, are not randomly scattered through the forest but tend to be concentrated in particular areas, principally those with the greatest amount of public use - around the High Lodge Forest Centre, for example, and in the vicinity of the Santon Downham offices.

The other great change which Figure 37 clearly shows is the steady shift towards felling in `organic coupes'. In 1970 the forest landscape was dominated by straight lines - by a pattern of rectilinear rides and compartment boundaries. Today this layout still exists in many areas but is rapidly being obliterated by the adoption of the new felling policy. The landscape of the forest thus continues to develop, reflecting changes not only in the attitudes and approaches of its managers, but also in the priorities and lifestyles of society as a whole.

Postscript

Postscript

Thetford Forest is a landscape of contradictions and curious paradoxes: and the more we learn about its history, the more paradoxical it can seem. Its role in nature conservation is one striking example of this. Planted for the most part at the expense of open heaths, its immediate effects upon wildlife were almost entirely negative. Of course, as we have seen, the extent to which the serried rows of conifers really replaced an untouched, `natural' landscape can be exaggerated. Much of the heathland had been but recently created, by the abandonment of arable land, while even the `virgin' heaths were the result of human interference with the natural environment - the product of an environmental disaster in remote prehistory. Nevertheless, the planting of the forest did radically alter an environment which had, in many places, remained virtually unchanged for millennia. Within the afforested areas the characteristic flora of Breckland was largely destroyed: and although there was an initial increase in the numbers of birds the range of species present changed rapidly. The distinctive Breckland birds - whinchat, stonechat, partridge, lapwing, stone curlew, woodlark and nightjar - declined, and were replaced by more common species like wren, hedge-sparrow, robin and jay.

Since the 1920s and 30s, however, both the forest itself and the landscape of the surrounding areas of Breckland have gradually changed. On the one hand, with the revival of agricultural fortunes in the post-war period, and the widespread adoption of irrigation, large areas of heathland have been converted to arable. Today, the only really extensive tracts of unploughed grassland and heath remain within the Battle Training Area, a large block of country to the north of Thetford, largely surrounded by Commission land, which was acquired by the army (and depopulated) during the Second World War. Elsewhere, the heaths now survive, for the most part, as small, discontinuous pockets, some of them nature reserves like Wretham Heath. In all, less than 8% of the area of Breckland now consists of heathland, and much of this is under-grazed and poorly managed. There is little doubt that the area now occupied by Thetford Forest would have been put to the plough in the post-war period, had it not already been acquired and planted by the Commission.

The intensively-farmed arable land surrounding the forest is of little conservation value. The forest itself, on the other hand, has gained steadily in wildlife importance. Its rides have become refuges for plants once common in Breckland, and the pines themselves, as they mature, have become a haven for crossbills and the red squirrel. As we have seen, current management practices are designed in part to encourage wildlife, reducing the size of felling coupes and ensuring a range of habitats through careful phasing of the felling programme. The forest may not be as ecologically important as the heaths and brecks which it replaced: but compared with the farmland which surrounds it today it is a sanctuary for wildlife.

Other curious paradoxes and ironies concern the forest's human history. Although it is essentially a modern environment, it contains many features dating from periods long before its creation. Forest Enterprise, increasingly aware of its responsibilities towards the cultural heritage in its care (as well as towards the natural environment), has recently supported a programme of archaeological survey work which has revealed the extent to which early earthworks survive in the forest - ancient barrows, old warren banks, and much more. Yet the forest has preserved traces of Breckland's early history in a number of less obvious ways. The names of places and features long gone - Santon Warren, Brandon Park, Parsonage Heath and the like - are liberally scattered across the featureless green blocks used to denote pine plantations on modern Ordnance Survey maps. More importantly, the rectilinear pattern of rides and compartment boundaries within the forest was not an entirely new creation of the 1920s and 30s. In many places it was based on earlier patterns of land-division: on the straight lines of pine and hawthorn established around the fields created when open fields and heaths were enclosed in the course of the eighteenth and nineteenth centuries (Figure 14). But the enclosure commissioners and land surveyors who created this pattern were themselves working within a long-exploited landscape: and they also preserved features from earlier periods, including parish and hundred boundaries laid out before the Norman Conquest, droves and trackways sometimes more ancient still. These, too, have often been incorporated within the network of boundaries defining the subdivisions of the modern forest.

Recognition of this fact presents a challenge to the forest's managers. Eager to enhance the appearance of the forest (and following extensive consultations with its many visitors) Forest Enterprise has, as we have seen, embarked upon a felling programme which will steadily reduce these continuities with the past. `Organic felling' may make good sense in the remote upland moors of Britain where forests were, for the most part, established at the expense of open land. Whether this approach should be adopted indiscriminately in a landscape more extensively moulded by the hand of man is currently a matter for debate amongst the forest's managers.

And discussions and debates on many matters will continue, as the forest develops new roles, and continues to change. Much has happened here over the last 75 years, as we hope we have shown. How this striking landscape develops in the future will, as in the past, be the consequence of the complex interplay of political, social and environmental forces, many as yet unknown, and unforseen.

Notes on Sources

Notes on Sources

The following brief notes are intended for those readers wanting to know where we obtained the information used in this book, or wishing to know more about particular subjects or issues.

Chapter 1.

For general accounts of the early history of Breckland, see in particular Roland Randall and David Dymond, `Why Thetford Forest? The Human and Natural History of Breckland before the early 20th Century', in Philip Ratcliffe and Jenny Claridge (eds) *Thetford Forest Park: the Ecology of a Pine Forest* (Edinburgh 1996), pages 1-15; John Sheial and Mark Bailey, `The History of the Rabbit in Breckland', in Philip Ratcliffe and Jenny Claridge (eds) *Thetford Forest Park: the Ecology of a Pine Forest* (Edinburgh 1996), pages 16-21; R.R. Clarke, J. MacDonald and A.S. Watts, `The Breckland', in H.C. Darby (ed.) *The Cambridge Region* (Cambridge 1938). W.G. Clarke's *In Breckland Wilds* (1925) is a haunting evocation of the pre-Forest landscape.

For the early settlement of Breckland see, in particular, Kate Sussams, *The Breckland Archaeological Survey* (Ipswich 1996); and P. Murphy, `Environmental Archaeology in East Anglia', in H. Keeley (ed.) *Environmental Archaeology: a Regional Review* (London 1984).

For the medieval period, see Mark Bailey, *A Marginal Economy? East Anglian Breckland in the Later Middle Ages* (Cambridge 1989).

For the post-medieval history of Breckland, see M.R. Postgate, *Historical Geography of Breckland 1600-1850*, unpublished MA Dissertation, University of London. For Breckland houses and gardens see Anthea Taigel and Tom Williamson, `Some early Geometric Gardens in Norfolk', *Journal of Garden History* (1991): and Taigel and Williamson, *Gardens in Norfolk 1550-1900* (Norwich 1990). The section on agricultural improvement is based on the following publications and documents. For the activities of the Dukes of Grafton, see West Suffolk Record Office HA 513/28, 13, 14, 16 and 17; and WRSO HA 513 28/9/1. For Lord Cornwallis, see C. Paine, *The Culford Estate 1780-1935* (Bury St Edmunds 1993), pages 23-27. The information about Parliamentary enclosure comes from an examination of maps and awards in the Norfolk and West Suffolk Record Offices. For marling on the Walsingham estate, see Norfolk Record Office (NRO) WLS LXI/1, 430 X 5; the quotation from Hugh Raynbird is from *The Agriculture of Suffolk,* (1849), page 118. For the problems with `warping', see NRO WLS XVIII/1, 478 X 9. The artificial irrigation of water meadows is discussed in Susanna Wade Martins and Tom Williamson, `Floated Water Meadows in Norfolk: a Misplaced Innovation', *Agricultural History Review* 42, 1 (1994), pages 20-27. The quotation about the expense of enclosure at Tottington is from NRO WLS XXVII/70/15, 415 X 5; that regarding the poor condition of the Breckland farms in 1786 is from NRO WLS XLI/2/20, 430 X 5. John Worledge's comments are from *Parliamentary Papers* 1821, VIII, page 544. Information about the Stanford Warren is from NRO WLS LXI/23/436 X 6. For the troublesome tenant, Abel Smith, see NRO Petre Box 17, 1. For Sylvanus Bevan see Arthur Young, *General View of the Agriculture of Norfolk* (1804), page 383. The West Tofts Sale Catalogue is in the Norfolk Record Office, MC 77/1/521/1. For the attacks by rabbits on the Buckenham Tofts plantations, see NRO Petre Box 17. The quotations from Massingham comes from *Through the Wilderness* (London 1935). Our thanks to Jill Ramsey, Susanna Wade Martins and Janet Lister for supplying many of these references.

Chapter 2.

For the general history of the Forestry Commission in Britain, see George Ryle, *Forest Service: the First Forty-Five Years of the Forestry Commission in Great Britain* (Newton Abbot 1969). Further information about changing government policy towards land purchases in 1919/20 can be found in the Public Record Office (PRO) at Kew: see, in particular, Minutes of the Forestry Committee, 6 December 1919; Forestry Commission internal memo, 12 May 1921; FC 18/73, 374/22, Vol 1; FC 14/36.

For the progress of land purchase in Breckland, see PRO FC 54386/4; FC 374/24; the Acquisition Report for the Croxton estate, Forestry Commission archives, Cambridge; and the following documents in that repository: FC L3/1/1; L3/3/9; L/3/3/15. See also P. Barnes, *The Economic History of Landed Estates in Norfolk Since 1880*, unpublished PhD thesis, University of East Anglia, 1984, pages 51-57.

For Didlington, Feltwell, Croxton, Downham, Culford, Brandon, and Mildenhall, see the Acquisition Reports and Files, Forestry Commission archives, Cambridge. The quotations about Lynford and Didlington are all from correspondence in these files.

For Lynford, see Forestry Commission archives, Santon Downham Office, Lynford Acquisition Report, Volumes 1 and 2; *Country Life*, November 28 1903; and the Lynford estate sales catalogue of 1924, formerly in Norfolk Local Studies Library (but since destroyed by fire). Other information about the initial purchase of the forest can be found in the 1959 *Working Plan* for Thetford Forest, chapters 4 and 5, in the Santon Downham archive.

For the cannibalization of country houses and estate buildings, and building operations in general, see J. Broach, `Building Operations: Thetford Chase', *Journal of the Forestry Commission* 10 (April 1931), pages 46-7.

The reminiscences of former Forestry Commission employees, Billy Steel and Arthur Cadman, recorded by Alec Douet and Kate Skipper in 1990, proved invaluable in writing this section.

Chapter 3.

The discussion of the progress of planting, and the proportions of different species used, is based on the 1959 *Working Plan*, chapters of 7, 8 and 10; on the stocking maps in the Commission's archive at Santon Downham; and on the *Annual Reports* of the Forestry Commission for the years 1927-1945. See also the Acquisition Reports for Downham Hall and Didlington; George Backhouse, `Thetford Forest', in H.L. Edlin (ed) *East Anglian Forests* (London 1972), page 7; Forestry Commission, *Thetford Forest: General Description*, First Edition 1972; and Norman Dannat, `Thetford Forest: its History and Development', in Philip Ratcliffe and Jenny Claridge (eds) *Thetford Forest Park: the Ecology of a Pine Forest* (Edinburgh 1996), pages 21-5.

For the development of the Forest's administrative structure, see: Rye, *Forest Service*, pages 63-70 and 98-103; *Working Plan* 1959, chapters 7 and 20; and the Forestry Commission *Annual Report* for 1948. For the development of smallholdings, see Rye, pages 185-194, and the bundles of leases (uncatalogued) in the Forestry Commission archives at

Santon Downham. The quotation about the marketing of smallholding produce is from the Forestry Commission's *Annual Report*, year ending September 30 1927, page 32.

For the forest labour camps, see Rye, page 58; Forestry Commission *Annual Report*, year ending September 30 1928, page 33; and David Colledge, *Labour Camps: the British Experience* (Sheffield 1989). Many of the quotations in this chapter are from this excellent book. The letters concerning the employment of labour camp inmates comes from the Lynford Acquisition File, Santon Downham archive. The reminiscences of Arthur Cadman, Graham Hobbs, Billy Steel, and Rex Witta, recorded by Alec Douet and Kate Skipper in 1990, have proved invaluable in writing this chapter.

Chapter 4

The main sources for this chapter are: *Working Plan* 1959, Chapters 11 and 16; and the successive *Working Plan Reports* for 1960, 1961, 1962, 1963, 1964, 1965 and 1966, all in the Santon Downham archive; R.B. Gibson, `Pre-thinning', *Journal of the Forestry Commission* 16 (March 1937), pages 113-4; G.F. Ballance, *History of Kings, Thetford, and Swaffham Forests,* (London 1951); and the files in the Santon Downham archive (uncatalogued) labelled `The East Anglian Pine Thinning Project'. See also Forestry Commission, *Britain's Forests*, pages 12-14; George Backhouse, `Thetford Forest', in H.L. Edlin (ed) *East Anglian Forests* (London 1972); and Forestry Commission, *Thetford Forest: General Description*, First Edition 1972.

For the creosote plant, see P.A.W. Overall, `Thetford Forest Creosote Plant', *Wood*, June 1968; and D. Small, `Thetford Chase Creosote Plant', *Forestry Commission Record* No. 4, 1960.

For the history of the Brandon Depot, see the excellent unpublished typescript in the Santon Downham archive, *A History of Brandon Central Depot 1946-1988* by Barry Griggs.

For changing patterns of work in the forest, see Inspectors Report, Thetford Chase, 1942 (Cambridge archive); the *Working Plan* of 1959; and the *Working Plan Reports* of 1960-68.

Once again, we have made much use of the reminiscences of former employees, recorded in 1990: especially Arthur Cadman, Graham Hobbs, Billy Steel, and Betty and Rex Witta.

Chapter 5

For fire control measures, see: `O.J.S.', `Forest Fires in 1933', *Journal of the Forestry Commission* 13 (March 1934), pages 9-16; R. Chard, `The Thetford Fire Plan', *Journal of the Forestry Commission* 28 (1959), pages 154-189; F.C. Dufton, `Thetford-Type Static Water Tanks', *Journal of the Forestry Commission* 8 (1952-4), pages 67-9; the *Working Plan* of 1959; the *Working Plan Report* for 1963. For deer, see Inspector's Report, Thetford Forest, 1938 (Santon Downham archives); the *Working Plan Report* of 1960; Rex Witta, `The History of the Deer of Thetford Forest', in Philip Ratcliffe and Jenny Claridge (eds) *Thetford Forest Park: the Ecology of a Pine Forest* (Edinburgh 1996), pages 141-9. Rex Witta's reminiscences, recorded in 1990, were especially helpful in writing this chapter. For rabbits, see J.J. Smith, `Rabbit Clearance in Kings Forest 1947-51', *Journal of the Forestry Commission* 8 (1952-4), pages 70-1; Forestry Commission, *Britain's Forests*, page 4; and the *Working Plan Report* for 1964. For the vole damage incident, see Thomas Hendrice, `Damage by Voles', *Journal of the Forestry Commission* 14 (March 1935), page 129. For *fomes* and insect pests in general, see John Gibbs, Brian Greig and John Rishbeth, `Tree diseases of Thetford Forest and their Influence on its Ecology and Management', in Philip Ratcliffe and Jenny Claridge (eds) *Thetford Forest Park: the Ecology of a Pine Forest* (Edinburgh 1996), pages 26-32. For pine shoot moth, see in addition the *Working Plan Report* for 1964, and J.M. Ross, `Study of Pine Shoot Moth Damage', *Journal of the Forestry Commission* 14 (March 1935), pages 56-64. For *Fomes*, see W.R. Day, `The Penetration of Conifer Roots by Fomes annosus', *Quarterly Journal of Forestry* 42 (1948), pages 99-101; J. Rishbeth, `Stump Protection Against *Fomes annosus*: inoculation with Peniophora gigantea', *Annals of Applied Biology* 52 (1963), pages 63-77; J.G. Wass, `*Fomes Annos*us in East Anglian Pine Sample Plots', *Journal of the Forestry Commission* 9 (1956), page 75; Inspector's Report, Thetford Chase, 1946 and 1949 (Forestry Commission Cambridge archive); *Working Plan Report*, 1963; and the bundle of letters, uncatalogued, labelled `Fomes' in the Santon Downham archive. Further information came from Billy Steel and Rex Witta, interviewed in 1990.

Chapter 6

Much of the information in this chapter comes from discussions with the present management team at Santon Downham, especially Sandy Greig. The earlier history of the Commission's attitude to wildlife, public and government comes from the *Working Plan Reports* for 1960-65. The comments about the poor state of the Santon Downham offices are from letters in `Santon Downham File 3', in the Santon Downham archives, 2.12.1963. The letter regarding Two Mile Bottom is in the Croxton file at the Cambridge archive, 1959-61: it concerns a dispute with Thetford Borough Council over the legal status of the land in question. For the quotation concerning more `aesthetic' felling and management, see L.M. Simpson and D.B. Henderson-Howat, *Thetford Forest Management Plan: a Conservation Review* (London 1985), pages 6-7. For the red squirrel, see John Gurnell, `Conserving the Red Squirrel', in Philip Ratcliffe and Jenny Claridge (eds) *Thetford Forest Park: the Ecology of a Pine Forest* (Edinburgh 1996), pages 132-140.

Postscript

For the immediate environmental impact of afforestation see W.A. Cadman, `Bird Life at Thetford', *Journal of the Forestry Commission* 15 (April 1936), pages 24-26. For the longer-term effects, see the various essays in Philip Ratcliffe and Jenny Claridge (eds) *Thetford Forest Park: the Ecology of a Pine Forest* (Edinburgh 1996), especially those by John Barkham; Christopher Hitch and Peter Lambley; and Rhys Green and Chris Bowden.

Index

INDEX